"Please, don't provoke me!"

"I think I will," Eliot replied, and swooped down quickly.

The kiss brushed Kate's mouth softly, like the touch of a feather, and was gone before she could react. "Well," he whispered, "slap me...like before."

Something strange was happening to her heartbeat, and she couldn't hold his stare. "Not today. Try some other time," she said lightly.

"Oh, I will," he promised. He was looking down her slender, relaxed body again. The intent, fascinated way he was staring made her warm from head to toe, and she moved uneasily.

"Beautiful," he said softly.

"I've told you I don't like men who flirt," she said sharply. Then suddenly the horrible fear came rushing back to her and she trembled, instinctively drawing away from him....

Books by Charlotte Lamb

A VIOLATION
SECRETS

HARLEQUIN PRESENTS

HARLEQUIN ROMANCE

These books may be available at your local bookseller.

Don't miss any of our special offers. Write to us at the
following address for information on our newest releases.

Harlequin Reader Service
P.O. Box 52040, Phoenix, AZ 85072-2040
Canadian address: P.O. Box 2800, Postal Station A,
5170 Yonge St., Willowdale, Ont. M2N 6J3

CHARLOTTE LAMB

man's world

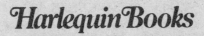

Harlequin Books

TORONTO · NEW YORK · LONDON
AMSTERDAM · PARIS · SYDNEY · HAMBURG
STOCKHOLM · ATHENS · TOKYO · MILAN

Harlequin Presents first edition February 1981
ISBN 0-373-10412-X

Second printing August 1982
Third printing October 1982
Fourth printing January 1983
Fifth printing November 1983
Sixth printing February 1984
Seventh printing February 1985

Original hardcover edition published in 1980
by Mills & Boon Limited

CHAPTER ONE

FLEET STREET was thickly clotted with traffic; throbbing bumper to bumper, the midday sun sweltering on metallic car roofs, bouncing back from windows, making the London pavements sweat beneath the feet of hurrying office workers dashing out to lunch. A small man with a gloomy face was meandering along wearing a sandwich board which bore a scarlet-lettered message. Kate did not have time to read it as she darted past him. Her blue eyes were fixed on a taxi she had seen heading that way. Its sign was lit, miraculously. She waved an arm, standing on tiptoe to catch the attention of the driver, and the large black taxi swerved in her direction with the insolent disregard of other traffic which London taxis can demonstrate when they see a potential fare. Another car blared its horn. A man put his head out of the window of a second and bellowed a muffled insult.

Kate stepped off the curb without looking and gave a cry of horror as she felt her heel sink. Looking down, she tugged unavailingly. Her fine heel had been trapped in a grating.

'Oh, hell and damnation!' The furious words were at odds with her carefully elegant appearance. Several passers-by stared in amusement.

'Stand still.' The voice at her elbow had a cool authority. She looked round, but the owner of the voice had knelt beside her to examine her shoe so that all she could see of him was the top of his head, the dusty gold of his hair gleaming in the sunlight.

She felt his fingers slide over her slender ankle. 'Can you stand on one foot? I can't extricate the shoe with you inside it.'

It was a ridiculous position to be in, and as she withdrew her foot Kate felt her flushed cheeks burning. 'Thank you,' she muttered, hoping she did not sound as ungracious as she felt. She wished she was a million miles away.

She had been held up leaving the office by an unexpected phone call and time was running short. Why did these stupid things happen when one was absolutely desperate to get somewhere on time? The shoes were new and had cost a fortune. She had seen them in a window in Oxford Street earlier that week and been captivated by them. Shoes were one of her few extravagances; she had very small feet and getting shoes in her size was not easy. These were Italian, made of soft supple leather and of a pale coffee shade which perfectly complemented the coral dress she was wearing. Kate had skimped on food to pay for them. She stood on one leg like a cross stork and stared as her rescuer fiddled delicately with the heel. Please, she thought, don't break it. As it was, the heel was bound to be scarred, that fine leather covered in weals. Oh, damn, she thought. That was what came of hurrying.

The taxi had drawn up beside them and she looked at it with fury. Now it would just drive away and with it would go her last chance of arriving on time.

She was wrong, however. Perhaps the hot weather had put the driver into a lazy temper or maybe he was just a friendly man, but he leaned over to stare down at them, his arms bare to the elbow, his shirt-sleeves rolled up and his collar open.

'Having trouble, lady? Need any help, guv?' He was a large dark man in his middle years and he grinned as he took in Kate's slender elegance.

The fair head lifted. 'I can manage, thank you, but you might put the lady into your taxi. She hailed you, I think.'

'Yes,' said Kate, throwing the man a hopeful smile.

'Right you are.' The man got out, came round and opened the back door of his taxi. 'Hop in, miss.'

Kate hopped with his help, feeling a fool, conscious of her flushed face and the stares of people walking past. The driver grinned at her. 'Never does to be too hasty. Next time you'll look before you leap.' It was good-humoured mockery and she gave him a little smile.

It wouldn't have mattered on any other day, but today she had a vital appointment and the last thing she had planned was to be late. She thought of all her careful preparations and could have screamed. She had been nervous all morning, her stomach full of butterflies, and now it looked as if the whole thing had been ruined. She glanced at her watch, and her heart sank. She had five minutes. She would never do it.

'Good work, guv,' the driver said outside. Kate eagerly peered out of the window. The fair head rose and she caught the grin her rescuer gave the driver. He climbed into the taxi and looked at her.

'I managed to get it out without ruining it,' he told her, giving her a smile which she could imagine had caused havoc before now. 'Your slipper, Cinderella.'

Going down on one knee, he extended the shoe and she slid her foot into it.

'Thank you very much,' she muttered, prickling as she felt him eyeing her long slim calf.

He lifted his head again and ironic grey eyes took in the faint but unmistakable hostility in her eyes. He was a long, lean man with eyes of a grey so light as to be colourless at times, although as he moved his head and the sunlight glinted on them she saw them take on a sudden blue gleam. His hair was thick and smooth. His nose had a classical line, straight, faintly arrogant. Kate's eyes did not linger on his mouth. She did not like the faint, amused smile it wore as he watched her.

'I'm sorry to sound churlish, but I have to rush,' she told him. 'I have a lunch date and I can't be late.'

He rose, leaned over to pull the door shut and sat down beside her. 'Where do you want to go?'

'The Apollo Club,' Kate told him.

He leaned forward. 'The lady is in a hurry, driver. Do the best you can, will you?'

The driver turned to grin at them. 'Watch my dust!'

They drew out from the curb, the engine throbbing. 'Optimist,' drawled the man beside Kate. 'In this traffic it could take twenty minutes.' He smiled sideways at her, the grey eyes teasing. 'If I'm lucky.'

Kate didn't smile back. She regarded him coolly. A flirt, she thought. That I do not need. 'I don't want to take you out of your way.'

He lifted thin dark brows which gave definition to his blue-grey eyes. 'Is that a hint that my company isn't wanted?'

'You've been very kind.' He had taken trouble over her shoe and she did not want to be rude.

'So you said.' He pushed his hands into his pockets and lay back in the corner lazily studying her. 'Do I hear the word "but" hovering on those delectable lips?'

Kate's eyes flared. 'Don't waste your ammunition on me. I'm not interested.'

He sat up, whistling. 'Ouch! What have we here, I wonder?' Taking his time in an infuriating way he ran his narrowed eyes over her from the sleek black head, styled so that the hair framed her face, down her slender figure in the coral dress. Kate stiffened as his eyes roamed. When they came back to her angry face, there was amusement in them, and that made her so mad she could have hit him.

Instead she did what she had done in similar circumstances. Taking a deep breath, she controlled her temper and eyed him exactly as he had eyed her. She had found in the past that it embarrassed even the most blatant of men. Today, however, it missed its mark. When she had coolly inspected him from the fair head to the polished black shoes she looked back at his face and found him grinning ear to ear.

'Devastating, aren't I?' The grey eyes mocked her.

She stared back at him without a hint of amusement, her face chilly. 'Sorry, no sale.'

He was in his early thirties, she suspected, which probably meant that he was married. A man with his undoubted good looks was unlikely to have escaped until that age.

'What have you got against men?' he enquired, his head back against the seat, dropping his lashes over his eyes, no doubt to hide that smile, but watching her through them in a way which made her spine prickle.

'Nothing,' she said clearly. 'I just don't happen to need one right now.'

'Where are you going in such a hurry?'

'Lunch.'

'Ah,' he murmured. She could see the glint of the light eyes. 'Is your lunch date male?'

'Is that any business of yours?'

'You're too worked up over it to be having lunch with an old school friend.' He was thinking aloud, his voice smooth, but he was watching her all the time as though trying to read her expression, gauge some reaction to what he was saying. 'Women never mind being late meeting other women. So it's male.' His eyes flicked down to her hands and she fought the impulse to push them out of sight. 'No rings, so you aren't married or engaged. Is he attractive?'

'I'm still waiting to hear what makes it your business.'

'You don't deny that I guessed right.'

'You can guess until you're blue in the face.' Her temper got away from her as she spoke and her voice was acid.

'You're a very nasty lady.' He gave her a wicked, teasing smile. 'And after all the trouble I went to for you!'

'I said thank you.'

'Is that all the return I get?'

'What do you want for performing a simple act of kindness? The Victoria Cross?'

He laughed, his eyes dancing. 'Do you work in Fleet Street?'

She surveyed him coolly. 'Do you?'

'This is a conversation, not ping-pong,' he pointed

out, the sun playing over the smooth hair, gilding it as he moved his head to stare at her.

They had arrived at the Apollo at last, and Kate sighed with relief. She dived towards the door and scrambled out on to the pavement, turning towards the fascinated driver. Something in his grin told her that he had been an attentive eavesdropper to that infuriating conversation in the back of his cab. 'How much do I owe you?' she asked him with a brief smile.

'I'll see to that.' The cool voice held a note which she angrily recognised. 'Wait for me, driver.'

Kate would have argued, but she was already late and she was not going to stand out here begging him for the favour of paying for her own taxi. If he wanted to squander his money that was his business.

'Thank you, how terribly kind of you,' she said in a saccharine voice, changing tactics and giving him a false and blistering smile. 'I'll never forget it.' Her eyes underlined that with a flick, but instead of withering him on the spot it just made him laugh again. Kate turned and fled into the elegant portals of the club, only to be stopped mid-flight by a uniformed porter with a stern face.

'Are you a guest in the club, madam?'

Kate was now ready to do battle with the next autocratic male she met. She looked at this one with fulminating wrath. 'Yes,' she snapped, 'I am.'

'The member's name, madam?'

Behind her she heard a footstep on the marble floor and her sidelong glance caught the gleam of gold hair. Stiffly she said: 'Mr Conroy.'

The man's haughty face altered slightly. 'Ah, yes, madam. Mr Conroy is waiting for you in the Guests'

Bar. Through the swing doors on your left, Miss Marchant.' He gave her a patronising little smile. 'Mr Conroy has signed you in.'

Oh, has he? Kate thought. Aren't I lucky? She turned and ran full tilt into the hovering shadow. Looking up into the grey eyes, she said crisply, 'Excuse me.'

He was looking at her in a very odd way. 'Dee Conroy is your lunch date?'

'You know him?' That threw Kate for a moment. Her mouth opened and she stared at him, then she shrugged. What was so odd about that? Half London knew Dee Conroy, at least by name, if not personally. Anyone could recognise his name. Dee frequently appeared on television and his face was sufficiently individual to stay in people's memories even if they could not put a name to it.

'I know him.' There was a frown pulling the thin dark brows together and the grey eyes held no smile now.

'Look, I'm in a hurry. Excuse me.' She turned and walked quickly through the swing doors, and this time she had no escort. What had brought that cold look to his face? she wondered. The charm and mockery had vanished and his face had been suddenly icy. Did he dislike Dee? That was not unheard of, of course. She knew several people who detested him. Dee could be scathing when someone fell down on a job and his method of expressing himself was not always charming.

She stood in the plushly furnished bar glancing around and Dee half-rose from a deep leather chair. Kate made her way over to him, an apology on her lips. 'I couldn't get a taxi. I am sorry.'

'It doesn't matter. I've only just arrived myself. Traffic was a real snarl-up on the way from Westminster. What will you have?'

'A Martini, please.' She sat down in the chair beside him and Dee snapped his thin fingers. A young waiter materialised with a respectful bend of the head. 'Dry Martini?' Dee enquired, and she nodded. He gave the order and the waiter de-materialised.

Leaning back Dee smiled at her. He was an energetic, lively man of around forty with restless, clever eyes and a sallow skin which was at the moment beautifully bronzed after a holiday in the Caribbean. His dark hair might earlier have been carefully brushed down, but now it was ruffled and standing in peaks. Kate had often watched Dee combing irritated fingers through his hair at conferences—it was one of the signs of impending explosion.

'We should do this more often,' he told her. 'I've been meaning to take you out to lunch for months, but I never seem to have a free day.'

'It's been a hectic year,' she agreed.

'One damn thing after another.' He grimaced. 'And this is supposed to be the silly season. God knows what it will be like when Parliament sits again.'

The waiter brought their drinks and fussed around her, arranging a scalloped mat before placing her drink on it.

'Mind if I smoke?' Dee was getting out a thin cigar, his thick dark brows arched enquiringly at her.

'I don't mind if you don't,' she retorted.

He grinned. 'Ah, another of your strongly held views. You have too many, Kate. It's time you cultivated a little tolerance.'

'There's enough of that around as it is,' Kate told him. 'If people didn't "tolerate" so much, the world might be a better place.'

'Your reading of the word tolerate doesn't quite match mine.' Dee was surveying her thoughtfully. The interview had begun, she realised. Dee had her under a microscope, his hazel eyes keen. He took his time lighting his cigar. 'How long is it since your husband died?'

He knew perfectly well how long it was—he had read her file. No doubt he knew it by heart. One of Dee's great gifts was a photographic memory which combined with instant recall made him a great editor.

She had slowed up now, the irritation of her chase to get here carefully controlled. She would play the match exactly as Dee intended. Quietly she said: 'Four years.'

He considered the glowing tip of his cigar. 'And you have no plans to marry again?'

'None.' None whatever, thank you, Kate thought. Not on your life.

The lazy hazel eyes flicked to her face, inspected the cool oval framed by elegantly shaped black hair. 'How old are you now?'

Another question to which he knew the answer and again she told him in a neutral tone. 'Twenty-six.'

'Are there any men in your life?'

Her hair bristled on the back of her neck. 'No.' What had that to do with giving her the job she wanted? Would he ask a male candidate if there were any women in his life? Would he, hell!

Dee gave her a tolerant smile. 'I know what you're thinking, you know.'

'Do you?' Of course he did. He was omniscient, like

most men. Always right, always able to see right through the little female head. She smiled sweetly at him. 'Really?'

He laughed. 'Oh, those big blue eyes. Yes, really. You're asking yourself what right I have to ask about your private life when all I should be interested in is your capacity to do the job.' He observed her pointedly. 'Yes?'

'It does seem slightly irrelevant.'

'Not so. When a man marries he doesn't give up his career. A woman usually does.'

'I shall not be marrying.'

He shrugged. 'I've heard that a thousand times before.'

'Perhaps you have, but I mean it.' Kate took a deep breath. 'My first marriage was hardly an advertisement for the institution. I wouldn't be fool enough to repeat my mistake.'

Dee's face sobered. 'I know the feeling.'

Dee's marriage had lasted for ten years, but a year ago there had been a divorce which had made his temper brittle and unpredictable for months. Kate looked at him with sympathy. Yes, no doubt he did know the feeling. She knew his wife, Judy, who had worked and still did in the women's page office. Kate liked her, but she knew, none better, that it was impossible to see into a marriage from outside. People who were perfectly charming on the surface could in private be positive fiends. She had learnt not to judge by appearances, especially where men were concerned.

She had finished her drink, and Dee glanced at her empty glass. 'Like another? Or shall we go in?'

'Let's go in,' she agreed, rising.

'The lunch here is a set meal,' Dee explained. 'They just do a roast—you can choose from lamb, beef or pork. They do have a salad with cold meat or cheese, as well.'

'The lamb will be fine,' she said, glancing across the spacious dining-room and realising that she was in very much a minority. There was only one other woman in the room; the rest were men in elegant lounge suits and self-satisfied expressions.

Dee caught her eyes and grinned. 'Yes, we're a chauvinistic lot. Women can be allowed across the threshold only as guests and only in small numbers. This is a hallowed place.'

They started their meal with a delicious home-made soup thick with chunky vegetables, served with crusty French bread. Dee ordered the wine without asking her opinion, she noticed, and maybe Judy Conroy had had good reason for that divorce.

'So you're embittered towards men,' Dee started out coolly, glancing across the table at her.

'I didn't say that.'

'You didn't need to—it shows in every word you say.'

She flushed. 'Embittered is the wrong word.'

'What word would you use?'

'Wary.' Very, very wary, she thought. A mouse which has been accidentally let out of a steel trap is very wary of walking back into one.

'Ah.' Dee broke off some bread. 'Good soup, this. Do you cook?'

'Brilliantly.'

He grinned at the snap of her tone. 'You must prove that to me some time. I love food.'

'You show no signs of it.' He was as thin as a rake, his energy consuming every scrap he ate no doubt. As deadlines approached Dee went around the building like a lion seeking whom he might devour, his tongue lashing anyone dragging their feet, his fingers crackling as though electricity leaked from their tips.

'That's why I eat here regularly.' He finished his soup and leaned back. 'I get sick of eating out of cans.'

The waiter arrived and removed their soup bowls before he began to serve their main course, carving deftly from the large haunch of meat, the pinkish slices falling thickly from his knife. Kate sipped her wine and listened as Dee talked about the previous edition. 'Too many literals are slipping by, but I feel like King Canute when I try to stop them. I wish we could put the deadline forward half an hour—the vans get out far too late.' He was making small talk until the waiter had left them, she realised, but she listened attentively, smiling.

For a few moments they concentrated on their food, then Dee asked calmly: 'If you did get the job, what plans do you have?'

'New brooms?' she asked, smiling at him.

'People always want to change things.' He considered her. 'And quite right, too. George has been a great features editor, but he's been there for fifteen years and it's time the kaleidoscope was given a shake.'

George had a fixed pattern, of course. There were certain ways of doing things, in his view, and he had gradually let the page stiffen into a sort of rigor mortis, quite without realising what was happening. He fought any changes which were proposed. During the last year he had smiled paternally at her whenever she suggested doing something new and said kindly: 'I'll be retiring in a year. Let's leave it, shall we?'

Kate had come prepared to be asked about her plans. She knew very well that it was the key question. She did not hurry to answer him, though, deliberately giving the impression that she was thinking it over.

'I think it would do no harm to rearrange the balance on the page,' she began quietly.

'In what way?'

'We don't carry enough features angled to fit the news. George prefers to steer clear of daily decisions. We carry too much stock.' George liked to work far ahead, laying in stores of features which had no current news angle but could be used at any time. The 'stock' drawer was crammed with stuff which he relentlessly pushed into the page.

Dee was not looking at her, but she knew he agreed with her because he had said much the same to George in the past. 'What else?' he enquired, making no comment.

'We lean too heavily to the political side. A weekly summary of political news is fine, but we don't need any more than that. I'd like to have more current affairs, social investigations rather than political.'

He nodded, still surveying his meal rather than her.

'And I'd like some wider based interviews,' she said with his eyes on his bent head.

Dee lifted his head. 'Such as?'

'As I said, following the day's news up—for instance that lady who got an award for industry the other day.'

Dee's eyes were hard. 'That belongs on the women's page.'

'Why?' Kate challenged.

'Because she's a woman.' He showed no hesitation in the blunt statement.

'And therefore of interest only to other women?'

'Yes.' Their eyes warred and she felt her colour rising. She fought to keep it down, to hold her temper down. It was not the first time she had clashed with him over this subject and no doubt it would not be the last.

'What she did should interest everybody,' she insisted.

'Marcia wouldn't agree with you. She always fights to keep the women's stories for herself.'

'Marcia is a great women's page editor, but I dispute the validity of a women's page in a newspaper these days. This isn't the nineteenth century. Women aren't housebound morons. They read the rest of the paper— why give them a separate page? You don't have a man's page. Or a dog's page.'

'I would if dogs could read,' Dee grinned, his eyes brightening. He eyed her with amusement. 'What you're suggesting would get me into dead trouble with Marcia.'

Kate knew that. She had had endless rows with Marcia in the past on the same subject. 'I'm not asking you to do battle with Marcia for me, but the features page would improve if I had a free hand.'

'Ah, a free hand,' Dee observed softly. 'I've heard those words before and they always mean civil war. If I removed the women's page where would I put the cookery articles and fashion?'

'In the dustbin,' Kate said furiously, catching fire and at once furious with herself. She had meant to play it cool and she dared not lose her temper.

'A lot of women like them,' Dee pointed out, watching her.

'They get them from magazines. A newspaper should be about news.'

'Marcia specialises in current stories of interest only to women—stuff about kids, adoption, sexual problems.'

'Men aren't interested in children?'

Dee looked amused again. 'Not riveted by the subject, no. Oh, come on, Kate, you know you're on a sticky wicket. Leave this—what other desperate acts do you want me to perform?'

'Listen, if Marcia gets all the female-angled stuff, that leaves our page unbalanced. Women do read it, you know!'

'You've already said they read the rest of the paper, so obviously they read your page. The point is—men aren't interested in cookery or fashion or the problems of the female anatomy, so why land them with stories they won't read? Put them on one page and men know which page to skip.'

'That's a sexist attitude.' Kate knew she was struggling with her temper. She had a quick, impulsive mind which took fire easily and she suspected Dee was deliberately provoking her. It was one of his ways of finding out the truth. At conferences he often trailed his coat merely to see what happened and who rose to the bait.

'Ah, the current jargon,' Dee drawled. 'So handy. Saves time which might otherwise be spent in thinking.'

'It's also shorthand for a whole range of attitudes

which typify the situation women today find themselves in,' she flung back.

'The trouble with women is they think emotionally.'

'What's that supposed to mean?' Her face ran with hot colour, her blue eyes blindingly bright.

Dee stared into them. 'Your views are coloured by your attitude to men.'

'My experience of men . . .' she began, and Dee cut in coolly.

'Has been traumatic—I know. That's why I find your thinking on the subject of the women's page somewhat suspect. You can't do it, Kate.'

'What can't I do?'

'Merge the sexes into one. Women aren't men and vice versa.'

'I never claimed they were—I only claim equality for my own sex. I don't want women turning into a pathetic pastiche of men. The world has been organised for the benefit of men for too long. When I got here today your porter tried to stop me coming in—I had to produce you for a credential before he'd let me cross his hallowed threshold. Earlier a man shared my taxi and insisted on paying—would he have done that for you? Would he, hell! He would have worked out a fair division with you, and he certainly wouldn't have tried to chat you up.'

Dee grinned. 'Oh, is that what's put you into a fighting mood? I wondered why you had an aggressive glint in your eye when you got here.'

Her eyes flashed. 'Nothing of the sort!'

'Fancied him, did you?' Dee asked, tongue in cheek.

'No, I didn't.' She glared at him. 'You see, it always comes down to the same thing in the end.'

'Why not? It's what makes the world go round.' Dee was laughing but Kate was not amused.

'And it's why I never get taken seriously as a journalist, only as a woman,' she bit out acidly.

Dee sobered. 'I take you seriously as a journalist. You're a damned good one. Why do you think I took you off news and put you into features as George's deputy? You've got a good nose for news and a first-class ability to organise it. Too many reporters let news walk right past them without recognising it. They have to be told what to go out and look for—they wouldn't know otherwise.'

Her temper cooled and she smiled at him. 'Thank you.'

Dee smiled back. 'I'm not making any promises. Of course, you're a strong candidate. You've shown you can do the job and you're on the spot. However, I have one or two other people to see.'

'I realise that.' She had not expected a firm decision yet. George had a month or two to go before he retired and Dee wouldn't be in a hurry to make up his mind. Several other people on the staff were interested, Kate was aware, but she was also aware that in the last year she had often run the department single-handed since George's health had not been too good lately. Her work had not gone unnoticed; Dee had several times said as much.

They dropped the subject, at Dee's instigation, and for the rest of the meal they talked about a whole range of other subjects, from the latest plays to a new biography of Churchill which had come out recently. Dee was a stimulating, amusing companion with a quick mind and a ready wit. Kate enjoyed his com-

pany, particularly as he did not make any attempt to
flirt with her.

Toby had been a flirt. Her experience with him had
coloured her whole attitude to men who used their
looks as battering rams. When she met Toby, Kate had
been eighteen, wide-eyed, innocent, bowled over on
sight by the charm and teasing smile which Toby
could use to such devastating effect. He had been twice
her age, a handsome man whose looks had been a pass-
port to success with women. She had fallen madly in
love and been amazed when Toby seemed to love her.
The first months of their marriage had been months of
great happiness for her. She had been incredulous at
her luck in meeting and marrying someone like Toby.

The awakening had come gradually. First she had
discovered herself to have married a man without con-
science or heart who pursued other women all the time.
Toby needed the excitement of the chase. He despised
women, she realised; they were merely the quarry he
pursued and once he had caught them he had no
further interest in them. Only Kate's innocence and
resistance had got Toby to marry her and, having done
so, he resented his hour of weakness. Kate slowly
realised that he was punishing her for having got him
to marry her. Toby had a cold, sadistic mind under
that golden charm. He made fun of her in public,
sneering at her, humiliating her. Her jealousy over his
other relationships merely amused him. He enjoyed
watching her flinch when he flirted with other women.
The final revelation had come when Kate tried to refuse to sleep with him during one of his extra-marital
affairs, and Toby had forced her brutally. It had
ended her feelings for him, but it had not ended her

marriage. Kate had left him, but he had followed her and her parents had begged her to go back to him. They did not know him and Kate could not bear to tell them the truth.

It would have made her humiliation and pain harder to bear if anyone else had known what was happening inside their marriage. Toby's smile had convinced her parents that Kate was just being childish. She had gone back to him and Toby had revenged himself by further sexual humiliation.

Kate learnt to pray that he would be too interested in someone else to turn to her. She found it hard to be in the same room with him. When they were in company she found herself watching the other people with disbelief—how could they be so taken in by that false smile, those bright teasing, cruel eyes?

When he was drowned in a yachting accident she was torn between sick relief and a feeling of guilt. She had hated him, by then, and she would long before have left him if she had not known that Toby would follow her and humiliate her in some way. He used other people's blinded reactions to him shamelessly. Everyone would have imagined that it was all Kate's fault. Toby's beautiful mask was too impenetrable unless one lived with him.

The only reason Dee knew about her fiasco of a marriage was because during the early days of his divorce he had stumbled drunk into her office late at night when she was working overtime on a special issue. He had blurted out his own misery about his wife and somehow Kate had found herself confiding her story to him. Dee had been very drunk, but he had remembered afterwards. His mind was as sharp as a knife even when he was under the influence of a bottle of whisky. Dee never forgot a thing, and he was one man whose attitude to her did not infuriate her.

Sexual advances from men made the hair stand up on the back of her neck; Toby had killed all sexual interest in her. After his death she had turned to a career with determination. She never meant to get involved with another man for the rest of her life.

CHAPTER TWO

WHEN she got back to her apartment that evening she found Oliver sitting on the doorstep with a Snoopy book in one hand and a sandwich in the other. He lifted his curly black head and gave her an innocent grin. 'Hi.'

'What are you doing here?' She inserted her key and pushed open the door. Oliver condescended then to get up and wander along the short corridor to the kitchen. Closing the door, a bottle of half-drunk milk under one arm, Kate followed him. 'How many times have I told you not to drink my milk? The shops are shut now and I can't get any more.'

He was rummaging through her cupboards, selecting things he fancied. 'No cheese? I'm starving!'

'You always are. Don't they feed you at home any more?'

'I'm broke.' Oliver had the intense self-absorption of the adolescent, his thin body always identically dressed in jeans and shirt, his manner vague. 'And I'm a growing boy, I need food.'

She surveyed him. 'Grow any more and Mum will have to keep you in the garden. What do you want money for?'

His blue eyes, so like her own, flashed to her. 'You're kidding.'

Kate laughed. 'Who is she? Or don't I know her?' It was always girls who drained Oliver's pockets. He had a never-ending stream of them passing through his life. Oliver fell in and out of love like a yo-yo, whizzing from girl to girl. A typical male, Kate thought, eyeing him.

'Her name's Primrose.'

'Yuk!' Kate grimaced, removing her last piece of cheese from his grubby paws. 'Oliver, leave my food alone. How much do you need?'

'How much can you spare?' A look of cunning crept into the blue eyes.

She considered the question and him. 'Two pounds,' she decided. 'Why should I pay for you to take girls out?' Oliver was a student, although as this was the summer vacation he had a temporary job doing summer relief work in offices. Kate was perfectly well aware that he was saving to buy a motor bike as well as paying their parents for his keep.

He graciously accepted the money with a winning smile. 'You're miraculous!'

She lifted an eyebrow. 'New word?'

'Word of the week,' he agreed solemnly.

'What was it last week?'

'Tedi,' he explained.

Kate waited, grinning.

'Meaning tedious,' he expounded.

'What a vocabulary!' Kate plugged in the kettle. 'Coffee?'

'Okay.' He hitched himself on to a high stool, his long legs draped over it like spaghetti. 'You look dressed-up-to-kill.'

Laughing, she explained, 'Interview.'

'Not a man?' Oliver had been fifteen when Toby died and had scarcely known him. Occasionally in the years since Oliver grew closer to her he had casually made some comment on the lack of men in her life. Kate ignored the way he was looking at her.

'Not a man, or only incidentally. It was with Dee Conroy.'

'Ah, the great Editor Man.' Oliver had seen him on television and secretly been impressed with him but he affected a cynical attitude to him in front of Kate in case she suspected as much. Kate was, actually, aware that Oliver admired Dee. Her brother was far more transparent than he realised. 'Is this the promotion you've been waiting for?'

'It would be promotion,' she agreed. 'George retires soon and his job will be vacant.'

'The King is dead, long live the Queen?'

'Funny.' Kate made the coffee and pushed him a cup. Oliver was far more spoilt than she had ever been. Her father was a busy doctor with little time for any family life, although he was a kind and patient man when he was at home. Her mother had adored Oliver from the day of his birth and although she had genuinely leaned over backwards to avoid favouritism somehow her feelings could not help showing. Kate did not resent the way her mother felt about Oliver. Casual, lazy, self-absorbed though he was, she was attached to her brother, but the long gap between them had made her more maternal than sisterly towards him, and her marriage had speeded up the natural adult processes shaping her mind. By the time Toby died, she had felt she was twice Oliver's age.

'You're not bad looking,' Oliver commented with lordly condescension, running a glance over her. 'Do you miss Toby much?'

She laughed before she could stop herself and caught his blue eyes staring. 'No,' she said quietly. 'Drink your coffee before it gets cold.'

'Change of subject. Yes, ma'am.' He saluted. 'Did you get the job, anyway?'

'I don't know. He has other people to see.'

'Did you feel hopeful?'

'I think I have a chance.'

'Not a bastion of male privilege, then?' Oliver grinned at her and she laughed.

'There are token women in most departments, but men still get the plum jobs. For every woman on the paper there are twenty men.'

'Sad,' Oliver mocked, knowing her views. 'You'll have to lead a crusade. Bring back the fiery crosses.'

'Give me my money back!'

He finished his coffee and leapt down with the grace of a gazelle. 'I'm off. Thanks for the food.'

'I must be crazy lending you a penny. I'll never get it back.'

'But I love you,' he teased, grinning as he headed for the front door. 'I'll give your love to Primrose.'

When he had gone the apartment seemed empty and very quiet. Kate had a light meal and settled down with a briefcase full of work she had brought home.

They were swamped with unsolicited material which had to be skimmed through in case any of it turned out to be usable. George had handed that job over to her soon after she arrived and she had done it ever since. George had ceased, indeed, to do any of the routine work. These days he concentrated on enjoying the leisurely lunches which his job entailed, arriving late in the morning, taking hours off in the middle of the day and departing early, leaving Kate to see the page set. George had, to all intents and purposes, abdicated from his role. He was just waiting for his retirement now, although he refused to allow her to act without his agreement.

George had not appeared by eleven next morning. When Mirry, their secretary, rose to go down to coffee she asked if she could bring a cup back for Kate. 'What about Mr Randell? Should I bring one back for him?'

'As he isn't here, there seems little point,' Kate said with a cool glance.

'Isn't he coming in today?'

'I've no idea. He hasn't informed me.' George sometimes just stayed away. Kate would not be surprised if he did so today.

Mirry was a very tall thin girl with soft fine hair and a whispering voice which made her sound as though she were always in a state of nervous alarm. In fact she was inclined to sulk, a girl with a difficult temperament, her mind rather slower than Kate's and her reactions always delayed. Kate never quite knew how Mirry would take anything. Weeks after making some incautious remark she would discover that Mirry was still brooding over it.

Mirry's eyes took on a typical wounded look. 'I'll

just get a coffee for you, then.'

Smiling at her, Kate nodded. 'Thank you, Mirry.'

When she had gone Kate settled back to work, only to be disturbed again by the opening of the door. Expecting George, she glanced over her shoulder and froze, recognising the tall, lean figure framed in the doorway. 'What are you doing in here?'

'I've come for the money you owe me.'

She stared in bewilderment. 'Money? What money?'

He moved into the room and closed the door, leaned on it and smiled at her. 'The taxi fare you didn't pay.'

She flushed. 'You offered to deal with it.' She snatched her bag up and opened it. 'How much do I owe you?'

'We shared the cab, so we'll split the difference. Eighty pence will cover it.'

She got out some coins and offered them to him. 'How did you find out where I worked?'

He wandered over and took the money, pocketed it. 'I have my sources. Now I'm restored to financial stability will you have lunch with me?'

'No,' she snapped.

'I was always taught to add thank you even after refusing an invitation,' he criticised, the grey eyes skimming over her with appraisal. 'You look very workmanlike today. I preferred you in the pink thing.'

'I don't dress to please you.'

His eyes teased her. 'You will.'

Her colour rose and her temper rose with it. 'Get out of here! I'm working. Who gave you permission to roam around the building?'

'Will you have lunch with me if I let you pay your share?'

Kate seethed. 'No.'

'Why not?'

'I don't want to.'

He grimaced, taking up a perch on the corner of her desk, his fair hair gleaming smoothly. 'What a tiresome female you are! I don't know why I'm bothering.'

'Neither do I.' Kate's manner was designed expressly for the purpose of keeping men at a distance and it usually achieved its object. 'And how did you get in here?'

'I work here.'

She was taken aback. 'I haven't seen you before.'

'There's a good reason for that.'

'Been hiding, have you?'

He laughed, and Kate found herself almost laughing back before she hurriedly tightened her mouth.

The amused way he watched her told her that he had noticed her weakening.

'I've been abroad,' he explained.

She studied him, and then suddenly she knew who he was; she should have recognised him before. His face appeared regularly in their columns. Yesterday she had been too intent on getting to that lunch with Dee to realise that she had seen that face before, but then of course their grey, grainy reproduction did not always do justice to faces. He did not look anywhere as good-looking in his photographs. Maybe he wasn't photogenic.

Her face had told him that she had finally recognised him. He arched those dark brows which did not match his hair, smiling.

'Eliot Holman,' she said slowly. 'Are you on a flying visit from the States?'

'Not so flying. I'm back for good.'

She hadn't known that and her face showed surprise. He had been their correspondent in America for the last five years and his column was widely read. Kate admired his crisp, elegant style. He wasted neither time nor words, but he always got his effect and he had been one of the most influential of their writers for a long time.

'No cheers?' he enquired in mock-sadness. 'Doesn't the thought delight you?'

She ignored that. 'Who's taking over in the States?'

'Bobby Riley.'

She showed no surprise. Bobby had just come back from a long stint in Australia and she had heard that he wanted to have a look at America.

'Will you miss America?' she asked.

'I thought I might,' Eliot Holman told her, his eyes on her. 'Now I'm not so sure.'

The implied flattery brought a spark to her blue eyes, but she bit back a caustic retort. 'What are you going to do now?'

'Moot point,' he shrugged. 'I'm writing a book, but I shall need to eat in the meantime.'

'It helps,' she agreed.

'And lunch with you would be very pleasant,' he continued smoothly. 'I like looking at something pretty while I eat.'

'Have a mirror handy,' Kate snapped.

If she had imagined she would dent his ego with a trite joke like that she was wrong. He grinned. 'What sharp little claws you have, Grandmother!'

She did not come back with the obvious retort to

that. Looking at her desk, she said instead: 'I'm working.'

'All through the lunch hour?'

'Probably.' It wouldn't be the first time. Her hours were supposed to be ten to six, but since George frequently left the whole of the routine to her she often found herself at the office until the page had gone down and come back again. Someone had to make sure that it had been correctly set. She glanced at her watch. 'I've got the morning conference in ten minutes. Do you mind?'

'I don't mind,' he told her calmly. 'I'll just come back. What time do you break for lunch?'

'Today I don't.'

The door opened and Mirry came in balancing a cup of coffee. She looked at their visitor with interest and he looked back, smiling in a way which made Kate want to hit him.

Mirry spilled some of the coffee as she put it down and Kate irritably mopped it up with a tissue while the two of them had a bright conversation behind her.

Mirry knew him at once. She had worked in the newsroom before she got this job in features and for a few moments Eliot Holman and Mirry swapped jokes about old friends and enemies. Then the fair head turned towards Kate. 'I'll pick you up at twelve-thirty,' he said, and did not wait for a reply before walking out of the room.

Kate said something under her breath and Mirry asked. 'What?'

'Nothing,' said Kate with a tight little smile.

'Are you having lunch with Eliot?' Mirry sounded incredulous, which was not surprising since Kate's aversion to male company in her private life was well known. The office rumour that she was an inconsolable widow had helped in persuading men to leave her alone. Mirry had a romantic streak which enjoyed the notion that Kate was nursing a broken heart.

'No,' Kate informed her tartly, 'I'm not.' She looked at her watch again and leapt up, grabbing papers from the desk. 'The conference!' she wailed, making for the door.

When she got to Dee's office it was already crammed and Dee looked severely at her over the top of his heavy dark glasses. He disapproved of unpunctuality as it dragged out the time spent on the twice-daily conference.

Kate only attended the conferences when George was absent. They were one of the routine tasks he liked to keep for himself. She sat down in a free chair between the Sports Editor and the Chief Sub-Editor and listened as the News Editor ran through his projected list of stories for tomorrow's edition. Some of them would have been discarded by the six o'clock conference, but the general outline would remain.

When Kate read out her own list of proposed features Dee made a face over one of them. 'Don't like that,' he said without much expansion. He had the final say where such matters were concerned, but he did not expect her to give in without a struggle. Dee enjoyed argument. It often made his mind work faster and sharper than ever.

Kate looked up. 'It's quite nicely written.'

'We had something similar a few weeks back and I thought it covered the ground quite adequately.'

That was true, but there was a reason why she had

slipped the feature into the page. Lowering her eyes to her list, she said casually: 'Judy has taken a new view of it.'

There was a little silence. Everyone in the room became engrossed in their hands. Kate glanced up. Dee looked at her coldly.

'Change it,' he said.

Kate shrugged. Judy's writing was always readable and often funny, but if Dee spoke in that tone of voice there was no point in further argument. Kate wondered how she was going to tell Judy. When the article came in she had liked it at once and told Judy how pleased she was, so she would not find it easy to explain why she was dropping it. They liked to take features from their own staff if they came up with them because it made staff happier and was also easier since they knew the style required and would not need so much editing.

When the conference ended Dee called her back as she was walking to the door. She stood beside his desk feeling like a schoolgirl in front of a headmaster. The others trooped out, giving them curious looks. Dee waited until they had all gone before speaking.

'Don't ever do that again,' he said icily.

Kate flushed. 'What?'

His hazel eyes were furious. 'You know what I'm talking about. I dropped that feature because of a legitimate reason and the fact that my ex-wife wrote it made no atom of difference. I don't bow to emotional blackmail, especially in public.'

'I didn't mean ...'

'Didn't you?' He used a biting tone. 'Just don't do it again.' He gave her a brief nod of dismissal and turned back to his papers. Kate walked out feeling two inches high.

She did not return to her own office. Instead she went down to see Judy. Sooner or later someone who had been at the conference was going to talk about the little scene which had taken place and Kate wanted to see Judy before someone told her what had happened.

Judy had a corner of the subs' room to herself since she worked on the women's page and nothing else. She looked up smilingly as Kate appeared.

'You look hot and bothered. George skipping again?'

Kate stood in front of her, blocking Judy from the rest of the office. The subs' room was a long, artificially lit room with two long desks in it. The men worked in a subdued silence, only talking now and then in low voices. Judy's desk faced the rest of the room. She was isolated from them as though she had some contagious illness, Kate thought crossly. She was also the only woman in the office.

Huskily she said, 'I'm sorry, Judy, I'm afraid the feature can't go in.'

Judy sat upright, her brown eyes fixed on Kate's face, narrowing. She was a very slender woman of thirty-six, her hair a rich chestnut which glinted gold under the electric lights. Kate had watched with sympathy as Judy's warm brown eyes chilled and her vivacious manner dulled under the months of estrangement from Dee. They still worked in the same building, but if they happened to pass in the office they ignored each other, so noticeably that it was painful to see.

'Why?' Judy asked, watching her.

Kate hesitated.

'Dee.' Judy said the name with cutting anger.

'We did have a similar feature recently, you see,' Kate said hurriedly. 'I'd forgotten. I'm sorry, Judy.'

'It's not your fault.' Judy brushed her apology aside. 'I know whose fault it is.'

'I really do think that he . . .'

Judy cut her off with a bitter gesture. 'Leave it.'

'He didn't know you'd done the feature,' Kate insisted.

Judy smiled icily. 'Dee knows everything, and he never misses a trick.'

'I love your writing,' Kate said hurriedly. 'Why not do a feature on . . .'

'No, thanks,' Judy snapped. 'I don't stick my neck out twice. That swine is only waiting to chop it off.'

'I'm sure he honestly didn't know until I told him,' Kate protested.

'So he did know?'

'Only after I'd told him, and he'd already said he didn't want a story on that subject again.'

Judy surveyed her. 'You usually hand in a typed running list when you go to conference.'

Kate paused, biting her lip.

'Yes,' Judy nodded, her smile twisted. 'You did this time, and Dee knew damned well who had written that article.'

'I'm sorry,' Kate mumbled again, wishing she had left well alone. But then if she hadn't told Judy someone would have done and it would have been an angled story Judy heard, making it sound much worse.

She walked back to her own office. Of course Dee must have known. Was that why he had rejected it? She had never known him to be spiteful. Surely Judy must be wrong. Dee was tough, but he was fair—in Kate's experience of him, that was, but marriage did funny things to people. No doubt Cinderella had discovered after the wedding ceremony that Prince Charming had a fetish about slippers. People could be very odd and very deceptive on the surface.

She had barely sat down at her desk when someone loomed up beside her and she regarded him with disfavour, her mood considerably darkened by what had happened in the conference.

'Hungry?' he asked amiably.

'No. I told you, I'm not coming to lunch.' Mirry had luckily gone off before Kate got back. There was no audience to be amused by Kate's argument with Eliot Holman.

'Kate, you're beginning to irritate me,' he said softly as he leant over her and stared into her face.

'What do I have to do to make you get my message?'

'What do I have to do to make you get mine?'

'I've got it,' Kate bit back. 'And it leaves me cold.'

'Has anyone ever told you that you've got eyes like little blue bits of glass?'

'Has anyone ever told you that you're boring them to death?'

He considered that, his head to one side. 'No,' he said at last. 'I can't say they have. They usually flutter their eyelashes and swoon.'

'That's not my scene,' Kate told him, wishing she did not find herself half-smiling because he had a voice which could charm birds off trees.

'Maybe you haven't tried it,' he suggested, a smile deep in the grey eyes. 'Do you ever smile? I mean, really smile? I've seen you give a phoney little grimace you intend to be taken for a smile, but it never gets as far as those beautiful blue eyes.'

'When you've gone I'll smile from ear to ear,' Kate promised.

He laughed at that. 'Bitch,' he said softly, staring at her. His eyes dropped to her mouth and the intent way he stared at it made her colour rise hotly.

His eyes flicked up to meet hers and his face was serious for a few seconds as he observed her, then he turned and without another word walked out of the room again. Kate sat there for several minutes wondering why she had a peculiar rapid pulse rate. She had not been affected by a man like that since she was first married to Toby.

It disturbed and alarmed her. She did not want to feel physical attraction to anyone. She did not want to get involved with any man; she just wanted to be left alone to do her job. She had had enough of the emotional torture a bad marriage could bring and her life since Toby died had been so calm and uneventful that it had seemed a halcyon period compared with what had gone before.

She forced herself to turn her concentration to her work again, but half an hour later she was disturbed again when Judy arrived, demanding that Kate lunch with her. 'Come on, put that stuff away,' she insisted. 'I'll buy a bottle of wine with the food.'

'Celebrating?' Kate asked brightly, although Judy did not have a joyful face.

'Let's call it an act of defiance,' Judy grimaced. 'I've just had a nasty little scene with Dee.'

'Oh.'

Judy caught Kate's eye and said flatly, 'Yes—oh. I shouldn't have gone along to see him. I knew what would happen. Every time we meet these days we savage each other and I ought to know better. Dee has a tongue like a razor blade. I expect you can see the scars.'

Kate did not want to be made a confidante in this business. She had enough bad memories of her own. But she liked Judy and her sympathies instinctively went to the female in this battle.

'Well, let's drink and be merry,' she said brightly. 'Shall we go to the Brasserie?'

'The very place,' Judy said with emphasis.

Over lunch and the suggested bottle of wine, Judy asked: 'How about you, Kate? Is it any easier yet?'

Judy believed, with the rest of the office, that Kate was a brokenhearted widow refusing to forget. Kate smiled tightly. 'I manage.'

'What else can we do?' Judy drank half her glass of wine and her skin flushed darkly. 'If it wasn't for Kevin I think I'd go crazy.'

'How is he?' Kevin was Judy's son, now aged eight, a boy with his father's thin build and restless energy but his mother's brown eyes and warm smile. Kate wondered how badly the divorce had affected him. It was always painful when children were involved in the break-up of a marriage.

'I'm never sure,' Judy admitted grimly. 'He hides his feelings well. On the surface nothing has changed, but of course there has to be some sort of problem underneath. It hasn't shown yet, thank God.'

'Does Dee see him?'

'Of course.' Judy kept her eyes on her glass. 'Every

weekend. I think he sees more of Kevin now than he did when he lived with us. He spent more time at work than he ever did at home.'

Had that been the problem? Kate watched Judy's thin face and could not read anything from it but a haunting sadness.

Someone paused beside their table and looking up Kate felt herself unaccountably flush as she met those pale grey eyes.

'So you do eat occasionally,' he observed drily.

Judy said in a lively way, 'Eliot! I heard you were back.'

Eliot bent to kiss her lightly. 'Hallo, Judy pet.' His voice was soft and gentle and Kate felt a peculiar coldness run down her spine as she saw the smile they exchanged. It made her feel excluded, an onlooker. She did not need to be told that they knew each other very well.

'Sit down and join us,' Judy invited. 'Have some wine.' She looked at the bottle. 'I think there's a glass left in that.'

'I'll skip wine,' Eliot Holman said, pulling up a chair. 'Waiter, bring us three brandies and coffee.'

'Not for me,' Kate announced coolly, rising. 'I really do have to get back. Judy, I'll settle up with you later. Thanks for the company. I enjoyed the lunch very much.'

She smiled at her briefly before walking off and she felt Judy staring after her in surprise. But when she passed the window opposite their table she saw Eliot and Judy deep in conversation, their heads close together, their faces intimately absorbed. How well did they know each other? she wondered, and got another shock as she again saw Eliot kiss Judy, especially when she saw the tears in Judy's brown eyes as he drew away from her.

CHAPTER THREE

THE mystery of George's unexplained absence was explained halfway through the next morning when Dee put his head round the door and said brusquely, 'Bad news, I'm afraid. George had a heart attack yesterday.'

Kate was shocked, swinging a pale face to stare at him. 'No! How is he? Was it serious?'

Dee shook his head. 'His wife says it was a mild one, but it was a warning. George won't be coming back.' He flipped a dark brow at her. 'Can you cope?'

'Of course.' She had been coping for months. 'Poor George! His wife must be very upset.' Kate had met her on several occasions—she was a thin quiet woman with an abstracted expression who let George do most of the talking. 'Where is he? I'd like to send flowers.'

Dee told her and she scribbled the name of the hospital on the edge of her blotter. 'I've sent some,' Dee informed her. 'From the paper. I'd send a bottle of whisky, but they'd never let him have it.'

She laughed. George was very partial to whisky. 'I expect they'll try to stop him drinking now.'

'Seven maids with seven mops couldn't do it,' Dee said drily as he vanished again.

Kate had George on her mind all day. She was feeling guilty about her irritation with him. She had been thinking dark thoughts about him and all the time he had been seriously ill. George had been kind to her when she first arrived. Now Kate felt sad whenever she paused to think about him. She should have been more patient. George had grown bored after fifteen years of doing the same job. It was understandable. She had been intolerant, self-absorbed, or she would have been more sympathetic with his restless dislike of doing anything. Years of daily use takes the edge off the sharpest razor. George had been a great features editor. As his excitement with the job faded so had his grasp of the work. It had all become dull routine, routine which George tried to avoid whenever he could.

For the rest of the day she had a series of encounters with people who had heard of George's heart attack and wanted more news and a chance to exclaim in surprise and sadness. Kate had rung his wife and spoken to her, found her tired and yet quietly optimistic. 'He'll have to stop work, of course, but it will be good to have him home every day. He sends his love.' Kate was able to pass on this message to everyone who asked for more details. George was well known and well liked around the paper. He spent far more time in the bar at their local pub than he did in the office and his fellow-drinkers were grieved at the prospect of his permanent absence.

In the elevator going down to the ground floor she found herself squashed in beside Eliot Holman. He did not speak to her, but from time to time the light grey eyes flicked sideways in her direction. The teasing smile seemed absent from them today. Kate did not pine over that. She had made it clear to him that he was wasting that charming smile on her and he had finally got the message.

She got the subway home, but just before she went down into the station she caught sight of Eliot Holman's fair head in the back of a taxi passing at that moment. Beside him sat Judy. Kate stood and watched the way their heads turned in lively conversation. As she let herself be drawn into the lemming-like stream of passengers she thought: well, why not? Judy's free and she's still very attractive. Eliot Holman had come back from the States and looked around for entertainment. Kate supposed she should be flattered that he had made a preliminary pass at her. She wasn't; she was merely contemptuous. She hoped he would amuse Judy, though. Judy needed to be cheered up. Dee had left her crushed, deflated. So long as she didn't take Eliot Holman and his intentions too seriously he might be good for her.

Towards the end of the following day Kate got a phone call from Dee. 'Will you have dinner with me tonight? I want to talk to you.'

About the job, she deduced, and accepted, agreeing to come along to his office later to meet him. 'We'll have a drink before we eat. I'm not sure when I can get away,' Dee added.

'I understand.' Dee's time was not his own. Problems had a habit of coming up just as he was about to leave the building.

After seeing the page she walked to the elevator and went up to Dee's floor. The corridor was silent as she approached his office. Most of the secretarial staff had gone and the building had taken on that special sound it had at night, the subdued hum which was far more exciting than the sound it made in the daytime when there were far more people about.

Dee's door stood slightly ajar. Kate was about to tap on it when she caught her own name and involuntarily paused. 'Kate isn't going to be happy about it, of course.'

'I realise that.' She knew that voice. Eliot Holman, she thought. What was he doing here? 'Would you have given her the job if I hadn't come back?'

Kate froze.

'Probably.' Dee sounded brusque which, in her experience of him, meant tension. 'She's done the job superbly over the last half year. George has been dropping out whenever he could and I couldn't blame him too much. I had a word now and then, but although he tried to put back his old interest it just didn't exist any more. Kate carried the office.' A drawer slammed as though Dee was charged with electric irritation. 'But as I said, faced with the choice between the two of you, I have to go for you.'

'When will you tell her?'

'I'm having dinner with her tonight. I thought it would come better in a relaxed atmosphere.'

Kate pushed open the door and both men swung to look at her in undisguised consternation. Eliot Holman was frowning, his face slightly pale. Dee flushed and met her eyes, grimacing.

'There's no need for the dinner,' Kate said coolly. 'I heard.' She turned her head and looked at Eliot. 'Congratulations.' She was so angry that she knew she had to get out of here before she blew up, but she just managed to speak in a level voice. 'Goodnight.'

'Kate!' Dee could move like greased lightning when he chose. He was across the office and beside her, grabbing her arm as she walked out of the door. 'I'm sorry you heard like that.'

'I know,' Kate said tightly. 'You meant to break it lightly. Well, the best-laid plans, etc.'

Dee held on to her and glanced over his shoulder at Eliot. 'Would you give me a few minutes alone with Kate, please?'

Eliot silently walked past them and Dee shoved the door shut. He still held her and looked down at her, his hazel eyes grim.

'I realise you're disappointed. You could have done the job very well and if a better candidate hadn't come along I'd have given it to you like a shot, but Eliot put in for the job the day he came back and I had to consider him. He's way ahead of you on all counts, Kate. He has more experience, he's known outside the paper, he has great contacts. A features editor needs contacts across a wide range of subjects, and Eliot has them.'

'I understand.' Kate understood all right. She kept her face very blank as she listened, but her blue eyes were icy.

'Do you?' Dee ran a hand through his dark hair. 'Kate, you're a very good journalist, but Eliot is out of your class. He wants a base in London so that he can start writing a book. We don't want to lose him, but the number of jobs open to him are limited. If we don't give him what he wants somebody else will—and we would be very sorry indeed to see him go.'

She nodded. 'I said I understood. There's no need to explain.' Pulling her arm free, she turned to the door and Dee slammed his hand against it with a crack that made the wood shake.

'Listen to me. I know you're angry, Kate, but try to

see it from my point of view. I have to think of it from the editor's chair, and the good of the paper comes first and foremost.'

If she said a word she would say too much, so she said nothing, her black head bent so that he could not see her face. She was so angry that her fingers had gone white with the tension coiling them. Kate's temper could flash beyond a white-hot barrier if she let it go. She was trying to stop herself from losing it, but she had to get out of here or she knew she would explode.

'There'll be other chances for you,' Dee said patiently. 'You're very young. Be patient and one day ...'

'Don't patronise me!' She flung up her head and stared at him scathingly. 'At least spare me that. The best man won.' She emphasised the word 'man' with bitter contempt. 'Can I go now, please?'

'For God's sake,' Dee bit out, 'don't drag your obsession with sex into this! Eliot got the job because he scores higher than you professionally, not because he's a man.'

'Your opinion of women was made painfully clear when you said that a news story about a woman winning an award belonged on the women's page because only women want to read about other women.'

'It was not a news story. It was an article.'

'It comes to the same thing in this case. Women are second-class citizens to you and always will be. Stupid of me to put in for the job, wasn't it? I'm acceptable to run the office, keep the routine moving, stand in for an absent boss while he takes three-hour lunches and clears off dead on six, but when it comes to actually appointing me officially I can forget it. If a three-legged donkey had come along you'd have given the job to him so long as he could prove he was male.'

'Don't be so damned ridiculous!' Dee was as angry as herself now, his thin face dark red, his hazel eyes violent.

'I'm a woman. What do you expect?'

'Nothing,' Dee snapped. 'You're right there, anyway. A woman thinks in zig-zags. You can't keep up with her. Logic has no meaning to them. I should have known better than to try to reason with you, Kate. There's only one approach you understand, isn't there?'

It was too sudden and too unexpected for her to have warning. He slammed her against the door and brought his mouth down in a punishing kiss which held no trace of emotion, only an angry desire to hurt and humiliate. Dee's thin hands held her against the door, biting into her shoulders, and his mouth oppressed her until her furious struggles lapsed from sheer exhaustion.

He let her go and straightened, his skin an angry red. Kate looked at him, her blue eyes leaping with rage.

'*You bastard!*'

She walked out, slamming the door. Eliot Holman was outside. He stared at her intently and she knew he had heard every word of the row, had known what followed. Kate walked past him without looking at him after one brief, contemptuous glance.

She went back to her office and typed out her resignation. It was a curt, bald letter which only revealed her anger in the absence of any expression of regret. Signing it with her full name, she dropped it into her out-tray and got up from Mirry's desk.

Eliot Holman appeared in her doorway, the lines of

his face blankly taut. Kate walked round the desk and moved towards the door, ignoring him. Inspecting the scene of his triumph, was he?

He did not move out of her way. She halted and without looking at him clipped out coldly: 'Would you excuse me, please?'

'I want to talk to you.'

'I *don't* want to talk to *you*.' That was the last thing she wanted to do.

'That's too bad, because you're going to have to,' he told her with a sting in his voice.

'Nobody *has* to do anything.' Kate moved to wriggle past him and he sidestepped so that she found herself faced with his long, lean body, her nose almost touching the well-cut dark waistcoat. He was wearing a very elegant lounge suit and, knowing the usual form, she guessed he had come to the office today to have an interview with Dee. Dressed to kill, she thought ironically. Oh, yes. And now the matador had come to admire the corpse, had he? He could think again! She looked up angrily and the grey eyes were blue, a deep violent blue.

He clamped her arm with one, long powerful hand and forced her, struggling furiously, back across the room.

'Get your hands off me! Who the hell do you think you are?'

He caught her chin with his other hand and thrust her head back so that her face was tilted towards him. The angry blue eyes focused on her mouth, inspecting it clinically.

'You'll have bruises there tomorrow,' he told her coolly.

'So will you have bruises if you don't let me go!'
Kate was hotly flushed, partly with rage, partly with
embarrassment. He had no business referring to that
kiss. He shouldn't have been eavesdropping. How
dared he manhandle her in that calmly arrogant
fashion?

Still holding her arm, he leant over and picked up
the letter to Dee lying on the top of the papers in the
out-tray.

'Put that down!' She grabbed for it and he held it
out of her reach.

'No prizes for guessing what that says,' he observed
with a twist of the mouth.

'It isn't addressed to you.'

'Your resignation?'

'Mind your own business!'

He smiled tightly. 'I thought so. I'm beginning to
guess the way your mind works.'

'Oh, yes, typically female,' Kate flung back angrily.
'I'm transparent to your keen male brain.'

'You react emotionally.' He tore the letter in half
and dropped it into the wastepaper basket.

'How dare you? How dare you?' Kate was so furious
she was almost incoherent, her words blurring together.

'Why resign before you have another job to go to?'

'I'll find one.'

'I don't doubt you could,' he drawled, staring down
at her.

'How flattering. Am I supposed to curtsey?' She
wasn't letting him soft-soap her and her eyes told him
so with a flash of rage.

'You're on a three-month contract. You would still
have to work that out.'

'Like hell! I'll just forfeit my pay.'

'Got a private income, have you?'

His sarcasm made her stir in helpless wrath. She had a little money in the bank, but it wouldn't last for ever and of course she couldn't afford a gesture like walking out now tonight, but her pride wasn't going to let her admit that.

'Would you mind letting me go?' She looked up at him and found him watching her closely.

'Make me,' he said in a soft voice deliberately calculated to infuriate her.

'All right,' Kate retorted through her teeth. 'You're bigger and stronger than me—big deal! If you expect me to feed your ego by uselessly struggling to get away, forget it. If that's what turns you on go ahead, prove that I'm the weaker sex. I hope you enjoy it.'

'I do,' he told her with a flick of his lashes which sent his eyes skimming over her tense, slender body and brought them back to her hot face with taunting amusement. 'You make it very enjoyable. I'm sure Dee got quite a kick out of it, too.'

Her hand flailed towards his grinning face and he fielded it, mid-air, casually, confidently, still smiling. Slowly he forced her arm down and moved closer so that his body touched hers, bending her back until she was off balance and had to support herself by leaning on the desk.

Kate stared into his face with bitter distaste. 'Go ahead, enjoy yourself.' Twice in one evening, she thought, her teeth gritting. Or had Dee put the idea into his head? And Dee claimed he was above sex prejudice? The minute you challenged them they reacted instinctively by imposing their physical superiority to prove that you were not their equal. That was how their minds worked. There was only room at the top for one sex and any woman who thought otherwise had to be shown that she was wrong. Toby had found it easy to humiliate her. He had had a shallow, narrow mind, but he had always been able to force her to submit to him merely by exerting the bodily strength which made him, to his mind, her master.

The grey eyes stared down into hers, narrowed and hard, as though he were able to read the bitter rebellion inside her head.

'What makes you imagine I'd enjoy kissing an acid-tongued little bitch like you?' His voice took on a drawl tinged with distaste. 'I'd have to be hard up for female company to want you.'

'I'm desolated,' Kate snapped.

'So I notice.' He was smiling again and the grey eyes mocked her. 'You are very obvious, lady.'

'So are you.'

'Am I?' He observed her with his head to one side in a way which she was beginning to recognise as typical of him. 'You know what I'm thinking?'

She met his stare aggressively. 'Yes.'

'I doubt it.' He sounded very amused and Kate didn't like the way he said that. The note of patronising superiority made her spine prickle as it had the day they met. If there was one thing she could not stand it was being spoken to in that authoritative, confident way by a man.

'Don't you talk to me like Moses coming down from the mountain,' she flared. 'You have no divine right. Will you let me go?' It was undignified and humiliating to struggle against his easy strength, but the edge of the desk was digging into her back and she was sick of being manhandled.

He shook her, without extreme force. 'Listen to me, you maddening little vixen! I put in for this job before I set eyes on you. I'm sorry if you feel I've stolen a march on you, but that's the way things happen sometimes. You can't win every fight.'

'Some of us can't win any of them. Women start out with too many handicaps.'

'Dee wasn't swayed by my sex.'

She laughed.

His hands tightened. The grey eyes were sharp. 'He might have been swayed by yours, on the other hand.'

She stiffened, staring at him. 'What's that supposed to mean?'

He smiled sardonically. 'We both know what it means. Dee wouldn't bother to take a man out to dinner to explain gently why he hadn't got a job. A polite letter would have been enough for anyone else.'

'Of course, women are so delicate and easily hurt, aren't they? They just aren't built for the hurly-burly of the newspaper business.'

'Cat,' he said with a dry smile.

'Dee still didn't give me the job although he admitted I could do it perfectly well.'

'I pulled rank on you, sweetheart.' He admitted it bluntly, staring at her. 'I'm sorry for you, but I wasn't backing out of the way to please you. This is a competitive business. If you can't stand losing, don't gamble.'

'I can stand losing on merit, but not on grounds of my sex.'

'You lost on merit.' Eliot Holman's voice cracked

like a whip. 'Don't bolster your self-confidence by telling yourself fairy stories. I've earned this job. I've had ten years' more experience than you and I can do it better.'

Kate's face ran with colour. She bit her inner lip and felt blood seep into her mouth. Looking down, she asked politely, 'Now may I go?'

'Not yet. I want your promise to hold back on that resignation for three months.'

She smiled icily at him. 'Want someone to do all the boring work while you swan off to the heavy lunches, do you?'

His eyes glinted. 'You ask for trouble, don't you?'

'I wouldn't ask you for anything.'

'I'm looking at this from your point of view,' he told her, ignoring that crack.

'Oh, of course. How high-minded of you!'

'If you walk out now you're going to get the reputation for being a temperamental prima donna and you won't find it as easy to get another job as you think.'

'You mean Dee would give me a rotten reference?'

'I mean nothing of the kind. I'm sure he would be fair.' His eyes emphasised that. 'Dee is fair; I'd have thought you knew him better than to believe otherwise. You'd get a reference which would describe you in glowing terms, but you would still have to explain why you walked out at a moment's notice just because you didn't get a job you wanted. Your prospective employer would quite rightly ask himself if he could trust you not to do the same thing to him, and nobody likes to have staff who just walk out at the drop of a hat.'

Kate stared at the floor. He was right, of course. She didn't like admitting it, but he was right.

'Give yourself time to look around,' he went on. 'Never walk out on one job before you have another lined up.'

'Thanks for the advice.' Kate used a sting when she said that, but inwardly she knew it was good advice.

He released her and she stood up, her back aching. They looked at each other in silence, their faces guarded.

'I realise you're going to hate working for me, but you're going to have to put up with it until you get something else,' said Eliot.

Kate turned without answering. She didn't look back as she walked to the door, but she knew he stood there watching her. As she went down in the elevator her mind's eye was filled with the memory of those grey eyes, hard and speculative, watching her in a way which she found disturbing. She had merely shrugged him away when he flirted lightly with her, but something had happened between them while he was forcing her to listen to him. She had felt a shift in her own feelings, a tentative peculiar flick of the kaleidoscope which left her seeing him in a very different way. In the past four years a number of men had made passes at her and she had ignored them with ease. During the minutes while Eliot Holman imposed his will on her she had discovered new reactions beginning inside herself, and she found their novelty alarming.

Kate had existed in a neutral zone for so long that any emergence of a sexual awareness inside herself made her feel faintly sick. While she could look at all men with either indifference or downright dislike she felt safe. Eliot Holman had made her feel something else just now and her stomach crawled with a tense apprehension as she admitted it.

It was nothing so definite as physical attraction. It was merely physical awareness, a form of tension she had not felt for a long time. She did not like it. It threatened the safety of her guarded citadel.

She sat in her apartment that evening listening to the blue wail of a Gershwin record, her head propped on her hands, a brooding intensity in her eyes.

The ring at the doorbell made her jump, then she made a face. Oliver, probably, in quest of a further loan. Wandering to the front door, she opened it and looked at Dee with a changing face.

He put up a defensive hand. 'Don't hit me!'

Kate wouldn't smile. 'What do you want?'

He dropped his hand and shrugged. 'To apologise. I behaved like a swine. I lost my temper. I'll go on my knees if you let me do it in private.'

'I don't find it funny.'

'No,' he accepted. 'I know what you're feeling. I fulfilled all your lowest opinions of men, didn't I? Chauvinist to my back teeth.'

She studied him, then let the door swing open. 'Oh, come in.'

He followed her into the small sitting-room and glanced at the record player. 'Gershwin? You a fan?'

'I enjoy him.' She bent to switch it off and Dee said, 'Don't. I like it, too.'

Kate straightened and turned. 'Would you like some coffee?'

'Please.'

The music followed them, becoming now a playful pastiche, half classical, half jazz, the horns blaring above the romantic tone of the piano. Dee leaned on the wall, his thin body relaxed, his arms folded.

'Forgive me?'

Kate kept her back to him. 'Have I a choice? You're my boss.'

'You aren't going to resign?'

She looked at him over her shoulder, her blue eyes alert. 'Do you think I should?'

'I thought you might,' he admitted. 'But don't, Kate. We don't want to lose you. I promise there will be promotion for you later on—you'll get your chance, don't worry.'

She did not comment on that. There was a pause while she made the coffee. Dee took the tray. 'I'll carry it in for you.'

The Gershwin had ended. Dee flipped it and the music swelled out into the silence between them as Kate poured the coffee. Dee lay back on the sofa, lounging casually, his long legs stretched out. She gave him his cup and sat down beside him.

'I really regret what I did,' he muttered, staring into the coffee. 'I'm under a strain at the moment. I suppose I just broke out when you argued with me. At that moment you were a woman and I just took the easy way out by showing you I was a man. It wasn't planned. I could have kicked myself the minute you'd gone. Knowing you I guessed I'd put the lid on it.'

'I should have smashed a chair over your head,' she confessed.

He gave her a brief sideways smile which held faint mischief. 'You couldn't pick one up. You're too frail.'

She smiled wryly at the deliberate, teasing joke.

'You do understand why I had to take Eliot?' Dee asked seriously. 'I was offered a first-rate editor whom we might otherwise lose. I respect you, Kate, but I won't insult your intelligence by telling you that in a straight fight you have any chance against him. He's brilliant and highly respected and he knows everybody.' He paused. 'Working with him could teach you a lot. Eliot is way ahead of the field.'

Kate had calmed down sufficiently to nod. 'I know.'

'You won't go then?'

She shook her head. Dee broke into a vivid smile, his thin face alight with it. 'I'm damned relieved. I was afraid you were going to walk out with your nose in the air.'

'You'd have deserved it.'

He gave her a teasing look. 'For picking Eliot?'

'For trying to put me down by showing me I was just a woman.'

The sting in her voice made him grimace. 'That tells me what a swine I am. I'm sorry, Kate. Hit me if it makes you feel better.'

'I might enjoy it too much,' she retorted.

Dee's eyes sparkled. 'So might I.'

There was a peculiar silence between them as they both digested that. Kate felt her face flushing.

'Sorry,' Dee muttered. 'Habit.'

'That's all right, you can't help thinking in sexist terms.'

'Don't patronise!' But he was laughing.

They drank their coffee in an almost amicable silence. Dee glanced at the record. 'What other jazz do you like?'

'Would you call Gershwin jazz?'

'He straddles both continents, doesn't he?' he agreed.

'I'm not keen on hot jazz—too strident. I like my music to be musical.' Kate got up and flipped over a pile of discs. 'I suppose I'm catholic in taste, but it has to be easy on the ear.'

Dee was studying her slender outline by the lamp which haloed her in soft illusion. 'I like you in jeans. Makes you look younger, less buttoned up.' He caught the glance she threw him and added tartly: 'And don't tell me I'm indulging in sexist chat again—I know you want to pretend otherwise, but the fact remains, you're a female, and I can't avoid noticing that.'

'It hadn't escaped me.'

He grinned. 'No. Not much does, does it? Little bright-eyes.'

Kate came back to the sofa and sat down to turn and stare at him. 'Why are you under a strain, Dee?' she asked curiously.

He sobered. 'Judy.' He ran both hands through his untidy hair. 'Every time we meet up it ends in a shooting match. Judy knows me well enough to find a mark with every bullet. We had a real beauty this morning. The other day Kevin told me he wanted to go to France again—we went there last year and he enjoyed it. I suggested to Judy that I pay for them both to have a fortnight there and she blew up like an overheated geyser. I kept my hands off her with great difficulty.'

And then when Kate argued with him Dee had lost the control he had somehow kept while he was fighting with Judy. She considered him, seeing the lines of strain around his restless eyes and mouth.

'Are you ...' She broke off. You didn't ask that kind of question.

Dee gave her a harsh smile. 'Oh, yes,' he said,

answering as if she had finished the question. 'You don't just shut off that sort of feeling.'

Frowning, Kate asked tentatively, 'Why the divorce, then?'

'Ask Judy.' Dee stood up with a violent jerk. 'I've asked her and I still don't know why. She just suddenly turned into a stranger.' The hazel eyes were darkened with feeling. 'Obviously there has to be someone else. What other reason could there be? God knows who it is—she won't even admit there is anyone, but there's got to be. We had a good marriage until she went to the States for a month. When she came back she'd changed and I watched our marriage fall apart at the seams.'

Kate thought of Judy's brown eyes with tears in them as she looked at Eliot Holman. She remembered his gentle voice and intimate smile.

'When did she go to the States?' she asked.

He shrugged. 'About eighteen months ago. She did a swap with someone on the *Clarion* desk over there— just for the experience of working on an American newspaper. Six months after coming back we were divorced—and don't tell me it was a coincidence. If I ever find out who the man is I'll kill him!'

Kate looked away from him. Had she imagined that look between Eliot Holman and Judy? And if she hadn't, what would Dee do when he realised that the man who had wrecked his marriage was working in the same building?

CHAPTER FOUR

ELIOT HOLMAN took up his new post a fortnight later. He had been given two weeks' leave, Dee told Kate. 'He needs it—the last months in the States were pretty hectic. I'm sorry to leave you carrying the department single-handed.' He grinned at her. 'But you're used to that. George has been a dead weight for months, hasn't he?'

Kate didn't answer. She was running her eye down a column and marvelling at the number of literals which had managed to creep into it. 'Listen to this,' she told Dee. 'The mumbo jet landed ... and here's another one ... do they do it for laughs or are they just being awkward?'

'Both.' Dee peered over her shoulder. 'I like that one.' His long finger prodded the proof. 'Stick that up on the board.'

'It's obscene!'

'The best ones are.' Dee straightened and moved away and she wondered if she had imagined that he had brushed his cheek against her own. 'See you,' he said as he strolled out.

Kate stared at his vanishing back. She liked Dee, but she did not want to get involved, particularly as she knew he was still hankering over Judy.

The office was busy during the fortnight before Eliot took over. Kate had neither time nor desire to accept the lunch invitations which would normally have gone to George. She passed them on to Dee who found someone to go to them or politely declined them, as he decided was most suitable.

On the Friday before Eliot arrived, Dee invited Kate to have lunch with him again. They lunched this time at a local restaurant much patronised by the staff. The Greek food was exceptionally well cooked and the prices reasonable. Eating a plate of octopus, Kate observed to Dee that it tasted like rubbery chicken.

'Do you like it?' he queried.

She laughed. 'I do, rather. It's certainly different.' Across the room she saw three of the reporters loudly arguing about football. They had been giving Dee and Kate curious, speculative looks and she wondered how long it would take the grapevine to spread the story. When Dee had her to lunch last time at his club it had been discreet and official. This time he had made no real pretence of it being either, although he had said he wanted to talk to her about Eliot's plans.

He caught her eyes on the other table and winked at her. 'They're wishing this table was bugged.'

'I don't want Judy scratching my eyes out.' Kate kept her gaze on him, watching him.

'Don't you? You think that likely?' He smiled twistedly. 'She has other fish to fry.'

'Maybe it's Judy you should be taking out to lunch,' she suggested. 'It would do no harm to talk to her.'

'When I can afford a bullet-proof vest I will.'

'It can't be that bad!' she protested.

'Can't it? Thanks for telling me!'

Dee's sarcasm made her smile. 'Have you tried?'

'I've got the scars to prove it.'

Marriage was a funny business, she thought. Neither Judy nor Dee were happy, but they didn't seem able to find their way out of the troubled minefield they had got into. Dee had admitted that he still wanted Judy, yet he was letting her go.

Kate watched him as he helped himself to more salad, the crisp green Greek salad which had an individual flavour often lacking in salads eaten in restaurants; chopped cabbage, onion, cucumber and pepper combining in a delicately mingled dressing of oil, lemon and vinegar. Dee was wearing a smart dark suit which emphasised his thin body and energetic build. He looked dynamic, a man temporarily at rest but happiest at full stretch, whizzing around making sure that everything on the paper was working at its full capacity, from machines to people.

He glanced up and caught her watching him. His smile made her jump. 'Don't brood over my problems. Forget them.' He offered her the salad bowl. 'Come on, stop looking gloomy.'

'You mentioned plans which Eliot Holman has,' Kate suggested as she helped herself to salad.

'Ah, yes.' Dee paused to sigh. 'You may not like them.'

'That won't surprise me.'

'No.' Dee laughed and gave her a teasing look.

'Don't tell me he's going to make it an all-male page.'

'Wouldn't you just love that?' Dee roared, his black head flung back. The reporters turned to stare.

'Actually I think I ought to leave it to him to tell you himself,' he went on, and Kate's brows drew together.

'I wonder why. Is it so revolutionary?'

Dee shrugged. 'He would probably prefer to do it himself. I don't want him to think I'm interfering in the way he runs the page.'

'You wouldn't do that, Dee, would you?' Her tone mocked and he gave her a wry smile.

'Don't be clever. I'm feeling too fragile today.'

'Why are you feeling fragile?'

'I had two hours with a union deputation this morning. Can't you see the boot marks all over my back?'

Kate laughed. 'Oh, that's where they came from! I thought you'd made a pass at Miss Wharton and got knocked flat.'

Miss Wharton was his secretary, a lady who had worked for him for years and ran the office like clockwork. Tall, piercing-eyed and formidable, she had, as far as was known, no weaknesses.

Dee laughed again. 'I wouldn't have the nerve. She eats men for breakfast.'

'Brave lady.'

Dee eyed her teasingly. 'Careful, Kate. In twenty years someone will say that about you.'

Kate did not like that. She glared at him and felt a cold shiver run down her spine. At the same moment there was a little stir as the door of the restaurant opened and two newcomers walked inside. Kate caught the peculiar vibration running through the other customers and looked round.

Judy walked down the restaurant towards an empty table without looking round, her vivid chestnut head high, but her companion halted to nod to Dee curtly before flicking a cold glance at Kate.

Dee's face was expressionless. He poured himself another glass of retsina and drank some of it. Kate wondered what he was thinking. If Eliot and Judy went on meeting like this it wouldn't be long before Dee did some simple arithmetic and realised just who had come between him and his wife.

In a small mirror on the wall above her head Kate could see Judy leaning forward to speak to Eliot. The warm green dress she wore gave an elegant line to her reflection. She had lost a lot of weight, though, Kate realised. So had Dee. They were both behaving like difficult children. Kate was somehow convinced that Judy wasn't indifferent to Dee. In the mirror she caught the quick look Judy gave to their table, saw a harsh frown cross her face and then the blank look reappear. Looking back at Dee, she guessed that he had looked at Judy a moment earlier.

He was staring at his glass now, twirling it in his hand. Looking up, he gave Kate a charming little smile. 'Did I tell you that you look enchanting?'

Normally Kate would have slapped him down for that, but there was a residue of pain in his hazel eyes and she didn't have the heart. She just gave him a faint, wry shake of the head and Dee shrugged.

'Do you want a paklava?'

'Just coffee, thank you,' she returned.

They drank their coffee slowly talking about yesterday's paper in a vague, abstracted way. Dee called for the bill and they left. As they walked away Dee said drily: 'Eliot's an attractive bastard.'

Kate didn't reply, and he glanced at her. 'Don't you agree?'

Kate met his eyes. 'Don't ask me.'

'Are you immune, Kate?'

'Immunised,' she corrected.

Dee frowned. 'What was your husband like?'

'I'd need notice of that question. It would take a

long time to list all the reasons why I never want to get involved with another man.'

Dee whistled under his breath. 'That bad?'

'He was a cold-hearted, shallow-minded sadist. And that was on his good days.'

Dee walked beside her for a moment. 'Why did you marry him?'

'I was eighteen and I was in love with him. It took me about six months to wake up. By then I was around forty-three, I'd say.'

'I'm sorry.' Dee touched her elbow lightly and she appreciated the delicacy which did not thrust a more intimate physical contact on her at that moment.

'I was lucky,' she told him. 'I could still be married to him.'

'I wonder if that's what Judy is saying to Holman,' Dee said with a savagery which made her look at him sharply.

He had used Eliot's last name. That struck her at once. Dee was beginning to think and from his expression his thoughts were not very pretty ones.

They parted at the elevator and Kate carried the picture of Dee's harsh frown with her for the rest of the day.

She spent the weekend at her parents' home, largely listening to Oliver and his girl-friend as they played heavy rock as loudly as the human ear could stand it. 'Why didn't I stay in my nice quiet apartment?' she lamented, and her father peered at her over his spectacles.

'Maybe because you miss us.'

She dropped a kiss on his bald head. 'Maybe that was the reason, but right now I can't believe it. If I gave Oliver some money do you think they'd go out?'

'Oliver's a parasite.' Her father folded his newspaper. 'You and your mother spoil him.'

'Me?' Kate laughed. 'What have I done?'

'The boy uses this house like a hotel.'

'He thinks it is one.'

'Your mother should have more sense.' The telephone rang and he groaned as he got up. 'No peace for the wicked!'

'Or even for the saintly,' Kate told his departing back. He grinned at her over his shoulder, but a moment later he was back. 'For you.'

'Me?' Kate got up in surprise. 'Who is it?'

'Male. Didn't give a name.'

Kate's mind leapt to Dee at once. She frowned and her father saw it with a faint frown of his own. Going out, she picked up the telephone. 'Dee?'

'No.' The voice had a bite in it. 'Eliot Holman.'

She held the receiver tightly as though it might fall if she didn't. 'Oh, hello.'

'I want to see you.' He sounded curt and her temper rose.

'How did you get this number?'

'I looked in your file.'

Her temper shot out of sight. 'How dare you pry into my file? What right do you think you have?'

'I'm your boss, remember?' She heard the satisfaction with which he said that and it didn't make her any more cheerful.

'I'd like to forget,' she said bitterly.

'I bet you would. We have to talk and the office is no place for this discussion. When can we meet?'

'I prefer the idea of the office.'

She heard his intake of breath and he spoke with a snarl. 'I don't. Can I pick you up now?'

'No,' she said. 'I'm busy.'

'What the hell is that racket?' he demanded.

'That is music,' said Kate, hoping she would be forgiven for the abuse of the truth.

'Your taste is depraved.'

Oliver wandered past in orange jeans and a purple T-shirt scrawled with a lurid message. He eyed Kate and mouthed, 'Editor Man?'

Kate shook her head, frowning. Oliver snatched the receiver away and growled in a deep voice, 'Stay away from her. She belongs to me.' Giving her back the phone, he bestowed a complacent smile on her and vanished.

'Hallo?' Kate said into the receiver, half furious, half on the verge of hysterical laughter.

'Who the hell was that?' demanded Eliot.

'My lover,' Kate told him sweetly. 'And he objects to me getting phone calls from other men, so I must go.' She put the phone down on Eliot's barked anger. Oliver came back with a large plate of cheese and pickles.

'Don't ever do that again,' Kate told him, pinching his ear.

He rubbed it, grinning. 'I bet that put some ginger into the conversation!'

'You're a silly little boy,' Kate said severely, going back to her father. Oliver made loud quacking noises and vanished back to Primrose and the heavy rock.

Dr Marchant looked up, his spectacles sliding down his nose again. He had a smile in his eyes which made her suspect he had heard Oliver's idea of a joke.

'Was that private or business?'

'Business,' said Kate, although she wasn't so sure

about that. 'And you're right about Oliver—he needs spanking.'

'Don't tell me, tell your mother.' He raised his newspaper again. 'I just pay the bills.'

Kate found her mother in the kitchen whisking white of egg and experimentally turning it upside down to check whether it would stay put. 'What are you making?' she asked.

'Meringues. Oliver fancies some.'

Kate looked at her with affectionate wryness. 'If he fancied some human heads you'd chop ours off, wouldn't you?'

Mrs Marchant looked offended. 'Are you jealous of Oliver?'

Kate perched on the edge of the kitchen table. 'Don't be absurd! Jealous of a thing in a purple T-shirt with words like that written on it?'

Her mother laughed. 'It's revolting, isn't it? He actually went out and bought that and then complains because he's short of money.'

'He was just rude to my boss on the phone.'

'Oh, dear.' Mrs Marchant added sugar and cut it in delicately.

'Did you hear what I said, Mum?'

'Of course I did. He's a naughty boy.'

Kate said firmly : 'You must speak to him. Get him to turn that noise down.'

'Yes, dear.'

'The neighbours will complain.'

'They already have. I told Oliver.'

'What did he say?'

'He promised to turn it down, of course.'

Kate cocked an ear. The thud of the rock music

continued undiminished. 'Mother, do you need a hearing aid?'

'Pass me the cochineal, will you, dear?'

Kate passed the small bottle and left. There was no point. She marched into the room where Oliver was sprawled on the floor with his small giggling girl-friend and turned down the volume. Oliver gave a squawk. 'Hey! What did you do that for?'

'I'm too young to go deaf.' Kate walked out and Oliver shouted after her, 'You're too young to wall yourself up either, but you do!'

Kate ignored that. She wandered out into the garden and sat on the freshly mowed grass cuddling their enormous marmalade cat. He dug his claws affectionately into her knee and she protested. The sun was hot and she was feeling sleepy. She lay back and inhaled the warm scent of the grass. The cat sat on her stomach and purred. The air was filled with the fragrance of mint and roses. A fly buzzed round her head and she sleepily waved it away before she slid down into a dreamless sleep.

Something tickled her nose and she flapped at it. It did not go away, however, and she came up through a lazy level of drowsiness to open her eyes reluctantly, expecting to find Oliver beside her.

Eliot Holman's grey eyes were blue today. For a few seconds she was still dazed, staring into them. His fair head bent slowly and before she had dragged herself out of sleep she felt his mouth touch her own. It moved delicately, sensuously, exploring the relaxed line of her lips, and Kate felt a flare of wild panic inside her chest. She jack-knifed upwards, pushing him away.

'Don't!'

Her voice was harsh, her sun-flushed face stricken. Eliot was staring at her intently, his eyes narrowed.

She took a deep, shaken breath which hurt in her throat. 'What do you want?'

'What would you do if I told you?'

She turned a biting glance on him. 'You can keep that sort of line for people who appreciate it.'

'You prefer the caveman technique, do you?'

For a moment she was blank, not following him. His eyes held a cold sarcasm. 'Dee seems to do all right. Maybe if I slapped your face and left bruises on you I'd get somewhere too.'

'Try it,' she said through her teeth.

He sat up and pulled off the denim jacket he was wearing, dropping it on the grass. 'No, thanks. I don't get my kicks beating women up.'

Her eyes flashed. 'Neither does Dee.'

He gave her a sardonic look. 'You rise to his defence with laudable speed.'

Kate drew in her lower lip, fighting down a desire to slap him. 'What do you want to see me about?' she asked.

'I've got plans for the page. If I told you about them in the office we would no doubt have a royal row, and I don't want secretaries flapping around listening to it. Mirry is a nice girl, but she gossips.'

'Dee told me your plans might surprise me,' she said.

'He didn't tell you what they were?'

She shook her head.

He stared at her fixedly. 'Are you sleeping with him?'

Her face tautened and the blue eyes became glacial.

'If I was it would be no business of yours, and I certainly would not be likely to admit it.'

'I've known Dee for years. He doesn't go around kissing women the way he kissed you unless there's a lot more between them than a working relationship.'

Kate stared at his lean, lounging figure. His fair hair glittered in the sunshine and the grey eyes had a piercing sharpness as he stared back at her. He was not a comfortable man, she thought. At their first meeting she had taken him for a casual, charming flirt of a type she recognised and disliked, but closer acquaintance had revealed other sides to his character. She did not like him any better, but she could not hide from herself the fact that she was conscious of him in a way she never was of men normally.

'No comeback?' he asked icily.

'I'm not discussing Dee with you.'

He took a sharp breath, his face tightening. 'You aren't the first, you know.'

That threw her. She stared, her eyes widening. 'What?'

He smiled in a jibing way. 'You mean you didn't know? Did you think it was love, true love?'

'What are you talking about?' she demanded.

'Dee Conroy and his women,' Eliot snapped. 'If you don't object to being one of a parade that's your business, of course.'

Kate brushed some grass clippings off her shorts and then wished she hadn't because it drew his attention to the long, slim legs exposed by the brevity of the shorts.

'Are you telling me Dee has had affairs?'

'At least one to my knowledge, and I doubt if that was the first.'

Frowning, Kate asked: 'Are you sure?'

'Certain. I know the lady in question.' He surveyed Kate with narrowed eyes, his face dry. 'You look as if I've shattered a dream. Sorry.'

She caught the jeering note in his voice and looked at him with dislike. 'I don't believe it.' Dee had never hinted that there had been anyone for him but Judy. But then would he have? Would he have confided a secret like that to her? Dee had told his side of the story in a way that made her sympathetic to him. Judy had never told her very much, but maybe there was a lot more to the divorce than Dee had hinted at.

'I don't have photographic evidence,' Eliot Holman said coldly. 'But you can take my word for it that Dee has strayed before.'

'Why should I take your word for it?'

He closed his mouth in a tight, hard line. 'My God, you've got it badly, haven't you? How long has it been going on? Is that why you were so sure you'd get the job? Paid for it in advance, did you?'

She caught him that time. Her slap nearly took his head off and he gave a thick grunt of rage as he reacted with as much loss of control as she had.

She was still off balance from hitting him and she sprawled backwards as he grabbed at her. Panting confusedly, she found him on top of her, his mouth bruising her lips open. Kate fought, writhing under him, her hands pushing and hitting him, but his hands seized her head and clamped it in a vice as he forced her to take his violent kisses. There was hardly a pause between one and another. His mouth twisted, devoured, dominated. She was suffocating, weakening. 'Is that how you like it?' he asked in a thick mutter. 'Am I getting to you now?'

The nightmare boiled up inside her head. She was being used again, brutally humiliated, neither her mind nor her body her own any more, a man's violent hands touching her with shaming insolence while she could only shiver and wish she were dead. The tears were running down her face from under her closed lids. Eliot's mouth felt them saltily trickle against his lips and he broke off the last demanding kiss to lift his head and look at her.

Kate took her chance to push him off and tried to make it to the house, but she did not have the time.

She bent over, shuddering, and dimly heard Eliot Holman swearing behind her.

When the appalling sickness was over she straightened slowly, her face white and stiff.

He was staring at his own feet and he was as white as she was now. 'Please go,' Kate said thinly. Her throat hurt and she felt very cold.

He lifted his head as if he was going to speak, then he walked past her without a word. When he had gone Kate went into the house and found her father whistling as he made himself some ice-cold lemonade. He looked round and his face changed. 'Kate! What is it?'

'I've been sick in the garden,' Kate said with a zombie-like flatness. 'I'm sorry, I couldn't make it into the house in time.'

'Never mind that,' her father said, pushing her into a chair. 'What made you sick? Have you a headache?'

'It was the sun, I think,' she lied. She had always lied to him. She had lied to him about Toby and she had lied to him about her own feelings when Toby died. It was easy to lie now. It had been hard at first. She had been very young, very naïve, and she had believed that her father could do anything. All through her childhood she had seen him in a godlike light, the pattern on which her expectations of men had been founded. When she began to discover that Toby was not the charming, pleasant man she had believed him to be, she had expected help and protection from her father, but instead she had found him disposed to see the situation through Toby's eyes instead of hers, and she had been deeply disillusioned.

Watching as he reacted with charmed warmth to the man who was making her life a hell on earth, she had been thrown back on herself. She had learnt that her father was as easy to deceive as anybody else. He was not an omniscient god; he was a nice, kind patient man who expected other people to be as decent as himself. When he came up against someone like Toby he was helpless, because the mask Toby wore was a brilliant illusion. It was designed to deceive and it got its effect.

Looking back, Kate saw that she had childishly resented her father's inability to pierce Toby's mask. She had been angry with him for years. Dr Marchant had failed her, in her view, and she had had to lie to him in consequence, her pride refusing to allow her to tell him what he could not see for himself. The time when she fled back to her home after Toby's sadistic rape, her father had been tender and comforting, yet every word he said made it plain to her that he laid the blame for the trouble at her door. 'I knew you were too young to get married,' he had said. 'But you chose him, Kate. He's still the man you claimed you loved so much and by running away from him you're ducking your responsibilities. Toby doesn't deserve this, you know. Go back to him and try again.'

Along with her mother, Dr Marchant had seen it all as a lovers' quarrel, one of the teething troubles of a new marriage. Toby had smiled and spoken gently to her in front of them. 'Maybe I was too hard on you, darling. It's my fault. I keep forgetting how young you are.' Oh, he had been convincing, and he had relied on the unspoken conspiracy between all men to make her father see it from his side.

She had come to see after that that one could not ask people to be other than they were—her father was a good man, but his knowledge of the world did not extend to men like Toby. In accepting the inescapability of her situation Kate had finally grown up, but she had found reality a very lonely planet.

She had learnt to rely on herself, prickly with pride, fierce with independence. Her nature predisposed her to hide from everyone what she felt. That was why she had allowed people to believe that she was still grieving for a man she had detested.

'I've told you before that you shouldn't ever go to sleep lying in the sun,' her father said as he helped her up to her bedroom. 'You may have slight sunstroke. The sun can be dangerous, Kate.'

Kate laughed unsteadily. 'Oh, life's full of risks.' There was a wild note to her laughter which made her father frown and look at her closely.

'You saw your new boss? He didn't stay long.'

'No,' said Kate. Long enough. Her stomach heaved again. Long enough.

Dr Marchant took her pulse and frowned. 'You'd

better sleep this off, Kate. I thought you had more sense.' He gently draped a quilt over her and bent to kiss her forehead. 'You look dreadful. Poor Kate! That will teach you a lesson, won't it?'

Her white mouth smiled in a twisted amusement. 'So it will.'

She lay shivering when he had gone. Whenever she tried to think about those moments when Eliot Holman held her down on the grass and imposed his mouth and hands on her, she felt a stab of fierce pain shoot through her temples. It had been a terrifying revisit to the past. The helpless, humiliating weakness of her body made her so angry she wanted to break things.

She no longer doubted what sort of man he was— he had made that very clear. Even though he had been so angry she had sensed the odd triumph in him, the growing excitement as he handled her. Swine! she thought.

Was Judy in love with him? Kate opened her eyes and stared at the blank white ceiling. Poor Judy if she was—and poor Eliot Holman if Dee found out and got his hands on him. Oh, Kate would like to be a fly on the wall that day. She would love to watch Dee smash Eliot Holman into powdered fragments. Dee's savage face as he talked about the unknown man who had wrecked his marriage had told her precisely what would happen if Dee ever found out.

Suddenly she remembered the thickness in Eliot Holman's voice as he asked her : 'Am I getting to you?'

She put her hands over her eyes to shut the memory out, but it persisted like a sick refrain.

He had got to her all right. He had put her through a wringer. She was chill and feverish, shivering and yet overheated. Her stomach cramped and her head ached. And on Monday she was going to have to go into the office and start working for him. How on earth could she face him after this? Just the sight of that lean, clever face was going to make her want to throw up.

CHAPTER FIVE

MIRRY was typing like a machine-gun when Kate walked into the office on the Monday morning. She looked up and threw a bright, 'Good morning. Lovely day.'

Eliot Holman was not in sight, for which Kate was grateful. It would give her time to pull herself together. She sat down at her desk and skimmed through the post. The phone rang and she picked it up absently. One of their writers moaned at her for ten minutes because a sub had taken a hatchet to his last article and Kate soothed and listened, agreed that it was incredible nerve, promised it wouldn't happen again. In the middle of the deluge Eliot arrived and she found it possible to give him a polite nod without giving any sign of the cramped sickness the sight of him caused.

He spoke to Mirry briefly, softly, and then sat down at his new desk and surveyed the order Kate had managed to restore after George's last day. George worked best in the middle of a tidal wave of papers. He enjoyed rummaging through them, throwing them all around like a manic clown. Out of the corner of her eye she watched Eliot Holman's brisk neat method of dealing with the backlog of stuff she had left on his desk. His eye flicked down a page and then it was discarded, mostly into the wastepaper basket and, having read it all herself, she did not disagree with his verdict. George was a magpie, hoarding stuff he must have known he would never use. Eliot Holman was cut on different lines.

He did not speak to her until Mirry had gone to coffee, then he swung in his chair and looked at her, although his eyes did not quite meet her own.

'Before we talk, I'm sorry.'

'I'd rather not discuss it.' Kate used a clear cold voice which had no particular expression and her face wore a frozen calm.

'I'm not discussing it, I'm just stating a fact. We have to work together for a while and we can't work efficiently with that between us all the time.'

'Very well, you've apologised. Now let's forget it.'

If the cutting sting of her voice made any impression he didn't show it. He got up and walked to the window, leaned there with his hands on the windowsill, his fair head outlined in glittering gold.

'We have to discuss my plans.'

'Yes?' Kate picked up her pencil and made a few meaningless marks on an article she was working on, and his voice cut furiously.

'Listen to me!'

'I am.'

'You can't listen and read at the same time.'

'You may not be able to. I can.'

He took a long, harsh breath. 'If you're going to be obstructive we're going to come to blows.'

'We already have,' she shrugged.

She regretted saying that as soon as she had said it. She didn't want to bring it up again any more than he did. Her tongue was always too quick, that was the trouble.

He was saying something under his breath that she preferred not to hear. She was accustomed to hearing men use language like that around here. As deadlines approached and tempers rose the language became violently explicit. It relieved pressure and let off steam.

She put her hands into her lap like a little girl. 'O.K., I'm listening.'

There was a pause while she felt him staring at her bent head. 'I have several changes in mind. Firstly, I want to run a monthly international page—we're too narrow in our view, we should take a look at the rest of the world.'

'Foreign won't like that,' she pointed out. If Dee could refuse to let her snatch stuff from Women's Page, why should he let Eliot Holman poach on Foreign's territory?

'They can lump it.' The dismissal was clear and unhesitating and already she knew he would get his way. Dee had fought her, but he wouldn't fight Eliot Holman.

'Our readers have no interest in what's happening in other parts of the world.'

'Don't be absurd! You're living in the past. We'll take it country by country, turn a magnifying glass on each one in turn, have articles on their economy, politics, recent social changes. It will bring in new advertising from abroad and make the readers more informed.'

The advertising would clinch it, of course. Dee

would have no trouble selling that aspect to the accountants. Advertising was the main prop which kept the paper afloat—anything that brought advertising in was fine with the powers that be behind the scenes.

She shrugged. 'What else?'

'More current affairs.'

He had paused and she looked at him. That had been one of her own aims and she suspected he knew as much. Their eyes met, guarded, wary, and he gave nothing away. If Dee had told him what she had wanted to do she would never guess from that shuttered face.

'No argument?' He had a dry note in his voice and the grey eyes flicked over her.

'You're the boss.' She enjoyed making that an insult, but he gave no sign that it had gone home.

The telephone rang and she swung to answer it. 'Kate?'

She recognised Dee's voice and said slowly, 'Oh, hello.'

'Dee,' he said, unnecessarily.

Across the room she felt Eliot Holman's attention riveted on her and wondered if he could hear Dee's voice. She put a hand over the earphone to muffle the sound a little.

'Yes?' she asked.

'You sound like melting ice cream. Eliot in?'

'Yes.'

Dee laughed. 'Oh, oh, is it war, Kate? Do I hear arrows whistling overhead?'

' A preliminary skirmish, perhaps.'

'Try to play it cool.' Dee was being incredibly understanding and she smiled.

'I am.'

'Kate, I've got tickets for *Scheherazade*—would you like to come with me?'

Kate stared at her desk, frowning. She recognised that this was a turning point. Both her lunches with Dee had been either official or at least a pretence of being so—this was different. It was a straight social invitation and she did not know if she wanted to accept it.

'Well ...'

'Please,' Dee said flatly. 'I took your advice and invited Judy. In fact, that's why I got the tickets—she loves the music. But when I rang her she refused, said she had a date tomorrow.'

Somehow the fact that Dee had told her frankly that he had wanted to take Judy and was only asking her as a substitute altered everything. A date tomorrow? Kate watched Eliot Holman walking across the office to pick up a large black leather diary from his desk. Was he Judy's date?

'Tomorrow?' she asked.

'We could have dinner first if we're quick.'

Eliot turned and the grey pierce of his stare shot through her. 'Thank you,' said Kate. 'I'd love to.'

'Thanks,' Dee muttered. 'I'll see you up here at around six. Eliot can put the page in for you.'

'I'll tell him,' Kate said softly before she put the phone down.

Eliot wore a harsh frown as she looked at him and before she could speak he asked curtly: 'What will you tell me?'

'That was Dee.'

He smiled unpleasantly. 'You surprise me.'

Her skin flushed, annoying her. 'He would like you

to stay late tomorrow to put the page in for us.'

'Why?' His lip curled. 'Or can I guess?'

'Guess away. It was Dee's request.'

He threw down the leather diary and it bounced on to the floor. He didn't pick it up, leaving it there as he walked to the window again.

'Our normal working arrangement has to be worked out. I suggest we stay late alternately. My weekends will be pretty busy, so I'd like you to do the Friday night. Sundays we can split between us so that you get a fair rota for weekends.'

Kate had always done the weekend work. George expected her to do it. Eliot was being ultra-fair in his suggestion. The editor always got a lighter share of the routine jobs. Reluctantly she nodded at him.

'Thank you.'

'You agree?'

'You're very generous,' she commented.

'Don't be sarcastic.'

She had meant that, but she looked at him irritably at his quick comeback.

'I wasn't being sarcastic. You're more than fair. I'm used to doing most of the late work and weekend work and I shall be glad to get off early now and then.'

'I'm sure you will.' His mouth hardened. 'So will Dee.'

Kate opened her mouth to snap back at him, but Mirry came into the room balancing cups in each hand and gave them both a beaming smile. 'Made it and not a drop spilt!' She put Kate's cup down on her desk and spilt some, grimacing. 'Sorry.' Eliot, Kate noticed, had got a saucer and none of his had been spilt. Mirry fluttered her lashes at him as he thanked her charmingly.

'My pleasure,' she cooed, and Kate could see that Mirry's sulkiness was not going to be so much in evidence now that George had been replaced by someone very male and attractive.

As the morning wore on Kate took on a wry expression as Mirry's breathless devotion became maddening. She hovered around Eliot like a bluebottle, buzzing excitedly if he smiled at her. When he went off to lunch Mirry turned to Kate and said with a deep sigh: 'Isn't he gorgeous?'

'Gorgeous,' Kate echoed derisively.

'Oh, you!' Mirry flounced, her long fine hair flying over her thin shoulders. 'It's time you came out of your shell.'

'It's time you went to lunch,' Kate told her, and Mirry looked at her watch and fled.

The telephone rang as she vanished and Kate got dragged into an argument over a picture they had used several days earlier. She worked as she listened, half her mind given to what was being said, making suffiently soothing noises to keep the caller happy. When she had hung up she turned her whole mind to what she was doing and forgot everything else.

She was surprised when Eliot came back early from lunch. She wondered how long such exemplary behaviour would continue. He glanced at her and asked why she hadn't gone to lunch herself.

'I've had some.' She had had a yoghurt and an apple at her desk, but that was none of his business.

His thin brows writhed upwards. 'That was quick.'

'I am quick.'

'Yes,' he said drily, and his grey eyes underlined the pointed sarcasm of the comment.

The Literary Editor sauntered into the room with his lanky body swathed in a pea-green sweater reaching to his knees. 'Aren't you hot in that?' Kate glanced out of the window at the brilliant blue sky, the glittering windows opposite. It was a baking summer, but then Roger always looked as if he had just arrived from the frozen north. He grinned at her, taking a pencil from behind his ear.

'Came to ask for more space.'

It was a common request and Kate girded herself for battle with him, but she needn't have bothered because Eliot drew himself out of his chair and Roger swivelled with an exclamation. 'Sorry, Eliot, didn't see you there. Congratulations. Heard you'd got the job.' Then he gave Kate a quick, embarrassed look, knowing that until Eliot's return she had been front-runner for the editorship.

Eliot returned the polite remark equally politely before getting down to brass tacks. Kate, excluded, listened and learnt a lot—she discovered what she had already suspected, that there was an iron hand inside Eliot's soft and silken glove. He charmed Roger by flattery and was very admiring of the way he ran his columns but wouldn't budge on the subject of more space. 'I'm sure you can cut it to fit,' he said, smiling, and Roger was smiling as he left, outranked, empty-handed.

Eliot met her stare and tilted an enquiring head.

'Clever stuff.' Kate did not bother to disguise the faint irritation.

'We haven't got the space to give him. It would

mean taking it from someone else and then we'd have two quarrels on our hands.' He paused. 'I want a layout conference at the end of the week. Call everyone in, will you? I suggest Friday morning around eleven.'

She nodded, making a quick note. 'I'll get Mirry to bring us all coffee, shall I?'

'I detest that muck they call coffee in the canteen. Can't we have an electric kettle and make our own?'

Kate opened her eyes wide. 'We could, I suppose. Would we get it on expenses?'

He eyed her scathingly. 'Funny. No, I'll buy one. I'd have thought you would have thought of it before. Don't tell me you like that dishwater they send up from downstairs?'

Kate had never thought of it. George was rarely around for coffee and Kate just accepted whatever Mirry brought her. She had known that if she wanted to make other arrangements they would all be left to her, and she had no time for coffee-making on top of everything else.

'We'll set up a float to buy coffee and milk powder,' Eliot went on.

'You've got it all worked out.' Kate smiled briefly to soften the sarcasm. 'Is that how you did it in the States?'

'American coffee is superb,' he said. 'Even in newspaper offices.'

'I wouldn't know.' Kate had never been to America. She had been to France and Italy and once to Aden on a lightning trip for the paper, but she was not a well-travelled girl.

'Never been there?' Eliot sat on the edge of her desk and looked at her. 'You must go. When I start the international editions we'll get a lot of free trips offered to us—maybe one will come up in the States. You could do that.'

Free trips, Kate thought, her eyes brightening. 'That would be exciting,' she told him. 'Wouldn't you like to go, though?'

'After five years there I think I know it well enough.' He paused. 'We shall have to do the first international edition together, you realise? I want to make sure you know what it is I'm after.'

Kate studied him warily. 'Together?' What did that mean? she asked herself in prickling suspicion.

His face was cool. 'I haven't made up my mind which country to do first, but whichever it is we'll go over there together. That way you can see what sort of angles I'm looking for and in future editions you can deal with it alone. One of us will always go.'

She had somehow imagined that it would all be done from the office. 'Will Dee allow all these trips abroad?' she asked.

His eyes took on that blue which she had come to recognise as a sign of anger or excitement in him. 'He knows my plans.'

And he'd better not try to stop me, she read, watching the hard bones of his face tauten. Dee had always been able to jolly George along, imposing his will on him easily, despite George's evasions and laziness. But Eliot Holman was a very different kettle of fish. Dee was going to find he had bitten off more than he could chew if he tried to take Eliot on in battle. She wouldn't mind watching that. It would be quite an experience.

'What sort of book are you writing?' she asked suddenly, wondering if it was fiction or documentary.

'A survey of American politics since the end of the Vietnamese war,' he told her.

'Light reading,' she commented.

His eyes had that blue again. She would have to watch for that; it was a dead give-away. Did he know that when he was angry however cool he looked on the surface his eyes flashed like summer lightning?

'You've got a nasty little tongue, haven't you?' Eliot put both his hands behind his neck and the lean out-line of his body had a tense control as he surveyed her. 'Careful it doesn't get cut out.'

She made her fingers into scissors and clicked them at him, starting to laugh, and after an odd pause he laughed back, relaxing.

'What angle?' she asked, and he lifted one brow.

'Come again?'

'What angle are you writing the book from? An English eye of American policies?'

'The Anglo-American situation in general,' he agreed. 'But putting it into the general context of the shift in American attitudes in the past five years.'

He was clever, she thought, watching his face as he spoke. The light-minded flirt she had imagined him the first time they met had been a gross distortion of the truth, or rather just one angle of his personality. He had to be a flirt, of course; she had been right there. Whatever the truth about his relationship with Judy he had known from the start that she was Dee's wife and that he was breaking up a marriage. That typed him, and Kate did not like men who shrugged when they destroyed things. The fact that he was also ob-viously very intelligent did not erase that side of his mind; it made it more damning. He should know better. It was easy to destroy things; it wasn't so easy to build them up again. And that applied to people too.

As the week wore on, she watched him closely and observed many other facets of his personality. He was hard-working, shrewd, clear-headed and quick to make decisions. He never shirked an argument and did not need to use brutal force to win, although she knew he was capable of it in certain circumstances—the day he used force on her in the garden at her parents' home she had learnt that. She had learnt other things about him during those moments, and she remembered them as she watched him dealing with the rest of the staff. Eliot Holman had a civilised exterior, but under that was another man—she had felt the build-up of excitement in him as he lay on top of her. He had found it enjoyable to do that to her. Were all men capable of enjoying force?

Now he had taken over, she was no longer eligible to attend the editorial conferences so she did not see Eliot in Dee's company, but she caught a glimpse of what was going on inside Dee's head on the evening when he took her to see *Scheherazade*.

They had a rapid, early meal before the performance. Dee took her to an Italian restaurant in Covent Garden which specialised in a delicious pizza served with salad. Straw-covered bottles hung in serried ranks over their heads and honeyed Italian pop music streamed from the loudspeaker just behind them. 'It's quick and edible,' said Dee, and then caught the look she gave the loudspeaker. 'Ignore the music—if you can call it that.'

'I like it.' She grinned at him as she said that. Dee was looking even more highly charged than usual and she wondered if he had been having another of his rows with Judy. The lines of strain seemed permanent these days.

'How are you getting on with Holman?' he asked.

Kate put down her knife and fork and met his eyes. 'We're keeping a polite truce.'

Dee went on with his meal before asking casually, 'Seen Judy lately?'

Kate did not need to make the connection. It was obvious. 'She hasn't been around for a few days.' Did he think that Judy was always in the office since Eliot took over? What did he think? She looked at him and wondered.

His mouth was taut. He poured her some more Chianti and then poured another glass for himself. She thought he was going to say something about Eliot and Judy, but when he spoke it was on another tack altogether.

'What do you think of Holman?' he asked later, after the performance when they were having a last drink before he put her in a taxi home.

'He's as good as you said he was,' Kate admitted.

Dee smiled at her warmly. 'Good girl!'

'Because I'm honest?' she asked wryly.

'It isn't a commodity much in circulation,' Dee told her with a twist of the mouth. 'I'd like some right now from Judy, but all I get is backchat.'

Kate looked at her drink 'What sort of truth do you want from her?'

'Who is it?' Dee broke out thickly and for a second the look in his face made her stare. She had seen him angry, she had seen him cold, but she had never seen him homicidal before.

'If you looked like that when you asked her, I'm not surprised she didn't tell you.'

Dee glared at her. 'You know, don't you?'

'How should I know?'

He held her eyes, searching them. 'Am I warm, Kate?'

She looked away. 'I don't know what you're talking about.'

He breathed heavily, his hands clenched on the table. 'If I find out I am, I'll kill him. They worked together years ago, did you know? She knew him before I did.'

Carefully Kate asked: 'Who are we talking about?'

Dee smiled savagely. 'Come on, Kate, you know perfectly well. I mean Holman.'

'Where did he and Judy work together?' she asked.

'Judy was subbing on the *Post* when Holman arrived as a cub reporter. When we were married she left the *Post*. I remember she told me then that Holman was a dazzling hit with the female staff.'

'I can believe it.' Kate was dry, her eyes sardonic. 'Mirry has palpitations every time he smiles at her.'

'But not you?' Dee looked almost grateful as he stared at her.

'Me?' Kate grinned. 'Now would I? I've got my reputation to think of, remember.'

'Reputation?' He looked baffled.

'As a man-hater,' Kate added drily.

Dee laughed. 'I've been confidentially told by at least six people that your heart is broken and you're a one-man girl.'

'So I am,' Kate said ironically. 'How right they are!'

Dee sobered. 'Poor Kate.'

'For God's sake, don't make me sound like a music-hall joke,' she flared. 'I'm happy as I am. It may surprise you to learn this, but life holds a lot more than the man-woman relationship.'

Dee changed the subject and they talked about the music they had just heard, the dazzling professionalism of the musicians, the flat taste of the lager which Dee had drunk in the interval. 'Warm and stale—next time I'll drink Coke. At least that would be kept cold.'

She picked up some other views of what was going on between Dee and Eliot Holman from the Sports Editor. She had lunch with him in the canteen a few days later and listened intently as he talked about Eliot. 'He and Dee get on like a couple of strange dogs. Conferences get very heated these days. Dee snaps at him as if he'd like to pick up the spike and stick it in his head. I thought they were old pals.'

Although he was talking casually she felt him watching her and guessed that the grapevine had picked up a rumour about Eliot and Judy. No doubt people were dying to know if it was true and if it explained Dee's aggressive attitude to Eliot.

Coolly she said: 'You know Dee. He always has a trial of strength with a newcomer.'

The man's fair-skinned face looked discontented. 'Yes,' he said without sounding convinced. 'I suppose that's it.'

As she left the canteen Judy walked into it and Kate caught the flicker of her brown eyes as she noticed her. It hurt when Judy turned her eyes away, pretending not to have seen her. Kate felt herself flush and hoped nobody else had noticed. What had Eliot told Judy about Dee's visits to the office? He had been down twice in the last three days, always with some valid reason and yet always somehow ignoring Eliot and talking to Kate in an intimate, deliberate way which embarrassed her.

Dee was being difficult. Kate had politely made an excuse to refuse his invitation to see a film with him. She wasn't getting dragged into the middle of that war. Dee was crazy about Judy and made no pretence of being otherwise. He was trying to use Kate for his own reasons and she wasn't having it.

Judy had been a friend of hers. Kate did not like being ignored like that. She wasn't going to make a public display of it by going up to Judy, though; that would be too risky. Judy might slap her down in front of everyone and Kate could hardly say to her frankly: 'Look, I'm not after your ex-husband. If you want him for God's sake climb down off that mountain and stop dating Eliot Holman.'

Every instinct in Kate's body told her that Judy still cared for Dee. She couldn't believe otherwise. If Eliot had told the truth and Dee had had an affair with someone, Judy's attitude was perfectly explicable, but it was counter-productive because it was driving a wedge between her and Dee when neither of them really wanted to lose the other. Judy could be playing tit for tat by seeing Eliot, but it was a very risky game.

It annoyed her when she got back to the office to find Eliot smiling down at Mirry as he dictated a letter to her. Mirry was looking like a stupefied kitten, her eyes enormous and glazed. Kate half expected to see her faint from sheer delight at the way that cool, smooth voice murmured the perfectly ordinary sentences he was dictating.

He glanced up and caught Kate's derisive, icy glance

and she saw the blue flash which told her he was reacting with anger. It pleased her. She liked sticking pins into his ego.

It was her evening turn, but when Mirry had gone, Eliot lingered with a blank expression. Kate looked round at him enquiringly.

'I've had a lot of response to my float of ideas for the international editions,' he told her briskly. 'I've decided to go to France first—as it's our closest neighbour it makes sense. We'll visit four cities, split the country in quarters, get a rounded picture. Paris, Marseilles, Bordeaux, Lyons. I'll make up a list of experts to do us some short summaries and we'll cover as much ground as we can.'

'When do you plan to go?' Kate was running through the schedules in her mind. 'Who will run the office if we both go?'

'I've talked to Dee about that. Roger can take over. We'll only be away for three or four days. If we make that a long weekend it will be easiest and Roger only has to work two days a week on his book page.'

'Dee agreed?'

Eliot's eyes were cold. 'Yes.' He gave her a long, unfriendly stare. 'He wasn't too keen on you going with me, but he agreed when I pointed out that unless you came with me the first time you wouldn't know how I wanted it done.'

'I expect Dee thought the office should be manned by one of us.'

'Oh, was that the reason?' He smiled nastily. 'I thought he might just be dead jealous.'

Kate felt two spots of red begin to burn in her face. 'Why should he be?' she bit back furiously.

'He hates me working with you, doesn't he?' Eliot's eyes pinned her to her chair, their stare hostile. 'I always had a good working relationship with Dee until I started working in this office and I don't need to guess why. Every time I speak to him these days he jumps down my throat.'

'Maybe you misunderstand the reason,' she said angrily.

'Nuts. I know when a man's showing signs of jealousy. He watches me like a lynx. You should reassure him, or do you like driving him out of his mind?'

'If Dee hates your guts that's nothing to do with me!'

'No?' He shoved his hands into his pockets and took a deep breath. 'Did you tell him what happened when I came to your family home?'

'No,' she said, shuddering.

Her voice left no room for doubt. He swore under his breath. 'I've been told I made people sick before, but I never thought it would actually happen under my very eyes.'

'I had sunstroke,' she said shakily. 'My father says sleeping out in the sun is dangerous.'

He laughed caustically. 'Do you think I'm stupid? You hated it, didn't you? Is that why you didn't tell Dee? But he knows something, otherwise why would he go for me like a rabid dog every time he sees me?'

Kate lifted her blazing eyes to his face. 'Of course, you couldn't guess, could you?'

Eliot stared with narrowed eyes. 'I just did guess.'

'You guessed wrong. Try again, and try a bit nearer home this time.'

He frowned. 'What the hell are you talking about?'

'Judy,' Kate flung. 'Remember her? Dee's ex-wife?'

There was a silence. Slowly Eliot said, 'Judy?'

Kate laughed. 'Oh, you're good! I loved the puzzled way you said that. You're in the wrong business—you should be on the stage.'

Eliot walked to the window and stared out, his back tense. 'So Dee has decided I'm chasing Judy, has he?'

'I think he imagines you've caught her by now.' Kate was so angry her voice was husky and she surprised herself by the fury she felt as she stared at his fair head.

'Well, well, well,' he murmured, spinning the words out in a soft drawl. 'And is that what you think?'

'I'm not paid to think about the private lives of fellow employees. It isn't my business. Judy's a big girl and I'm not her keeper.'

'But?' he asked when she had bitten off her words.

She was silent, her head turned away, and he added drily: 'Come on, I heard the "but" in your voice. You've got an opinion, all right. Let's have it.'

'But I thought she had better taste,' Kate snapped. 'Dee's worth fifty of you, and Judy must have a hole in her head.'

'You're so kind.' He was sarcastic, a cold smile on his face. 'You ought to be relieved. After all, with Judy otherwise occupied, Dee is all yours.' He laughed harshly. 'Until his roving eye roves elsewhere, at least.'

'If I were you I'd walk very wary of Dee. He's boiling up for a real row.' She gave him a smile as icy as his own. 'I wouldn't want to see that handsome face rearranged into a less than charming pattern.'

'How charitable to warn me. When am I to expect Dee to turn vicious?'

'Any day,' she said through her teeth. 'Laugh if you

like, but I wouldn't like to be in your shoes when he does go over the top. Dee can be violent.'

He gave her a twisted smile. 'As you know, I remember.'

Her flush returned and her eyes threw dislike at him. 'Leave me out of it.'

'Oh, you're very much part of it, lady, and you know it, despite the cool don't-touch-me air. That only goes for other men, not Dee, doesn't it? His technique must be better than mine.'

'Mind your own business!' Kate flung back angrily, reddening and hating the cynical way he was eyeing her.

'Coming from you, that's rich! I suppose it's your business if I date Judy?'

'Oh, go to hell! Date her if you don't mind risking getting your face kicked in when Dee loses his temper.'

Eliot leaned over her desk and gave her a cool, sarcastic smile. 'You love me, don't you, darling? You really love me. You're hoping for a ringside seat when Dee comes for me.'

'That's right,' she said, glaring at him.

'Are you still nursing a bruised ego because I got the job? Isn't that tough. Especially after all the trouble you'd gone to—Dee welshed on the bargain, did he?'

Kate picked up the nearest object and flung it at him. It happened to be her can of pencils and they bounced and clattered all over the floor as he ducked to avoid them.

She saw the cold flash of the grey eyes as he lifted her wastepaper basket and placed it on her desk in front of her. 'For when you're sick,' he said with a snap, then held her back against her chair and kissed her forcefully, bruising her lips open and invading her mouth. Kate was too taken aback for a moment, then she began to struggle violently. Eliot straightened, his face darkly flushed, and without a word walked out.

CHAPTER SIX

THE little incident seemed to be the last straw. Their relationship had been difficult, but now it became impossible. From then on the atmosphere between them was like the moment between a crash of clouds in the upper stratosphere, a humid sizzle which was followed by thunder and lightning. They worked side by side, either in a frozen silence or with a barbed exchange of tart remarks. Mirry was bewildered and fascinated, looking from one to the other like someone at Wimbledon, trying to keep up with the rapid volley of curt retorts.

Kate had always been famous for snappy remarks. Her hot temper and the chip she carried on her shoulder combined with her ready tongue to make her someone people avoided arguing with when her eyes flashed, but Eliot Holman showed no such restraint. He came back at her as fast and bitingly as Kate herself, and the way they snarled at each other made the office a less than restful place.

Kate was aware that Mirry, in common with most other people in the building, put her temper down to rage because Eliot had walked into the job she wanted. Having watched him at such close quarters for some weeks Kate was reluctantly forced to admit that Dee was right about him—he was brilliant, and far outside her class. If she had been in Dee's chair she would have done exactly as he did—given the job to Eliot. The admission was not grudging. Kate admired professional efficiency. If other things had not entered into their relationship she would have told Eliot as much, but she wasn't going to climb down in front of him when those grey eyes tore her apart every time he looked at her.

He had introduced his changes into the features department with gradual, competent ease and, despite a little grumbling, they had begun to accept them. From what Kate picked up in the canteen, though, Dee still sniped at Eliot at conferences, picking up every tiny slip and using it against him.

Whenever Kate saw Dee she realised what a strain he was working under, his features drawn, his eyes burning with the energy of a man under too much pressure who will not give way and is building up to some crisis.

One afternoon as she was hurrying back to her office after a long tussle with the music critic she saw Judy come out of another door. Kate paused, a smile ready, and Judy looked right through her with a stiff, cold face.

Kate felt as if she had been slapped across the face. Her smile withered. She walked on, biting her lip. Judy had undoubtedly heard that she was seeing Dee. The gossip, as often happened, was way behind the times. Kate had carefully not seen Dee lately, refusing all his invitations, avoiding his company. How could she tell Judy that, though?

Tense and disturbed, she walked into her own office and found Mirry and Eliot roaring with laughter at today's cartoon. They looked round and Kate went to her desk, ignoring them. Their laughter broke off abruptly. Mirry began to type noisily. Eliot returned to his own desk, but his eyes were cold when, a few moments later, Kate accidentally met them. She didn't care. Let him think what he liked.

Mirry left, as she always did, spot on six. It was Kate's late turn and she worked on in the mellow summer evening, feeling faintly peculiar, her head aching, her body tense. She had been feeling strange all day, although she could not put her finger on what was wrong.

'Kate, will you have dinner with me?'

The voice made her jump. She had been concentrating on what she was doing and when she looked round and saw Dee she stared at him blankly for a moment, trying to think.

'Dee——' she began, and as she spoke Eliot walked into the room, stopping dead as he saw Dee. The two men eyed each other as though a fight might break out at any moment. Kate had heard that Dee openly disliked Eliot, but now she saw an answering hostility in Eliot's harsh face.

Dee looked away from him and down at Kate. 'I'll wait for you in my office,' he said, and walked out.

She bent over the proofs. Eliot stood behind her and she felt him staring at her. Heat stirred in her veins. What on earth was the matter with her? She wasn't having an affair with Dee, whatever he thought, so why was she blushing like a schoolgirl?

'I'll finish for you,' he said suddenly. 'I wouldn't

want to hold up your evening with Dee.'

'It's my night.' She went on skimming down the
column, her pencil in her hand, but it was suddenly
taken out of her grasp. She looked up with furious
eyes.

'Give that back!' she snapped.

'Get your jacket on and go.'

'Look, if I want to swap turns with you, I'll ask.'

'For God's sake, don't argue over every little thing,'
Eliot bit out, staring at her.

'I didn't start the argument.'

'Oh, you never do, do you?' he said sarcastically.
'Butter wouldn't melt in your mouth. And don't turn
those big blue eyes on me—I know what they can do,
lady. I've got the burn marks to prove it.'

She snatched at her pencil and his hand closed
round her fingers. Kate looked up and felt her throat
close at what she saw on his face. They stared at each
other and a pulse began to throb hotly in her neck. If
he touched her with that look in his face she knew she
would be sick again. The colour all left her face.

He flung her hand down. 'Don't worry,' he grated,
'I'm not going to touch you. I might beat the hell out of
you.'

That made it worse. It rang too many bells. She saw
the force, the heat, in his face and tried to stand up,
but swayed on her feet. Oh, God, I'm going to faint,
she thought.

'All right?' His voice was terse, still angry.

She couldn't answer, struggling to retain consciousness. He pushed her back into her chair. She put her
head down on the desk and lay there until the drumming in her ears had subsided a little. What a fool

he must think her! The sleek black hair fell over her face, hiding it from him, but she felt him standing beside her, watching her, and she wished he would go because the trembling would not stop.

'You're in no condition to go out to dinner,' he muttered. 'You should go home.' There was a pause. 'Shall I ring Dee and ask him to come and take you home?'

She shook her head, slowly lifting it. 'I'm all right.' She wasn't and she knew it. So did he, staring at her white face and shadowed eyes intently.

'You look it.' That held savagery. 'My God, my effect on you is miraculous, isn't it? Is it some sort of allergy? I hope it doesn't spread. I don't want to be known as the man who makes women keel over whenever he goes near them.'

'I thought you were,' she said bitingly.

His eyes flashed blue. 'Ah, back on form, are we?'

A step made them both turn round. Judy stood in the doorway, her vivid hair glinting in the light. She gave them an odd look and Eliot said drily, 'Come in, darling. Take a look at one of my casualties. Would you say she was fit to have dinner with anyone?'

Kate's face burned with sudden, painful colour. Bastard, she thought. How can he? She couldn't look at Judy.

'That depends who it is,' Judy said curtly. 'Eliot, I wanted a word with you.'

'I'm just going,' said Kate, standing with a horrified realisation that she was very unsteady on her feet. The room was going round. Maybe she was really ill. It could be 'flu.

'Sit down.' Eliot shoved her backwards in an unchivalrous gesture which sent her down into her chair with a thud. She looked at him with rage.

'I'll be with you in a minute, Judy,' he said, and Judy without looking at Kate went out. Eliot dialled and said curtly, 'Kate can't make it for dinner tonight, I'm afraid.' There was a muffled outburst from the other end and Eliot cut into it, ' 'Bye.' He put the phone down and looked at Kate. 'Stay there. I'll drive you home when I've done the galleys.'

'Listen——' she began hoarsely.

'No, you listen,' he told her. 'You're ill—take a look in the mirror. I'll be back. Just stay in that chair and don't do a thing.'

He strode out, slamming the door, and she heard the distant sound of his voice talking to Judy in the corridor. Kate tried to look at the galley, but her eyes would not focus properly. She put her hands over her eyes, rubbing them. It had to be 'flu, she told herself. It was going round the building, a summer variety which came and went within a day or so but was nasty while you had it.

Eliot came back and she took her hands away. He lifted the galleys and took them to his own desk, and she dimly watched the rapid flick of his eyes as they moved down the columns. My God, he's fast, she thought. Accurate, too. He paused several times to correct something and went whizzing on in the same smooth way.

He flung the sheets into the out-tray and came over to her. Without saying a word he lifted her from the chair like a child, his arms round her waist. The room was going round in the same dizzying fashion.

She clutched at him to support herself, her head dropping on to his chest, hearing the strange muffled

thunder close beside her ear without realising at first
that it was the sound of his heart under the striped
blue and white shirt.

'What the hell's going on?'

Kate dazedly lifted her head to look round and saw
Dee's thin face through a muzzy cloud. He was staring
from the doorway, his face coming and going in the
oddest way, like an old-fashioned movie where the
heroine has been drugged. I'm ill, Kate thought. How
strange!

It seemed so funny that she giggled and Eliot looked
down oddly at her.

Dee moved across the office like a blue streak. 'Get
your hands off her!' he roared in a voice that made the
room bounce with sound.

Eliot let Kate slide back into the chair which she
did obligingly, her legs now quite beyond her control.

'She's sick ...' Eliot began, and Dee broke into the
sentence with a hoarse rage which had been contained
for too long and had broken out of all bounds.

'I'm sick, too, sick of watching you flirt with my
wife!'

'Leave Judy out of this,' Eliot told him. 'All I'm interested in at the moment is Kate.'

'You can keep your hands off her, too, you swine!'

'Make me,' Eliot snapped, and suddenly the hostility
between the two men was a raging fire, the flames
visible in both of them, their eyes sparring in violent,
uncontrolled hatred.

'Gladly,' Dee grunted as if it was an appalling relief
to let all his feelings out, his face deeply flushed.

Kate stirred, lifted her head on a neck which seemed
too frail to lift it. 'Don't, Dee!' She put up a hand

which wavered and fell back.

It distracted them for a second. They both looked at her and she tried to look at them, but they shifted peculiarly like people seen through water.

Dee went down on his knees beside her chair, touching her forehead lightly. His long thin fingers were very cool and she sighed with pleasure.

'Leave her alone,' Eliot said harshly. 'Judy is coming down again in a minute. I asked her to help me take Kate home and put her to bed. I don't want her seeing you here.'

'Isn't that too bad?' Dee bared his teeth in a snarl, turning his dark head to glare at him. 'I'm sorry Judy finds it a hardship to see me, but she'll have to grin and bear it.'

'You selfish swine, your affair with Kate has given Judy enough heartbreak already. You might have the decency to clear out so that Judy doesn't have to see you on your knees to her.'

Dee's head stayed turned, his neck muscles tightening. 'Affair with Kate? I'm not the one having affairs, Holman, and if I was, Kate would be the last one I'd pick!'

Dimly Kate thought: charming. She heard their voices and understood every word, but their faces were out of focus and distorted.

'Don't give me that! Everyone in the building knows. Did you think you could date her without anyone finding out? I doubt if there's a member of the staff who isn't in on the secret.'

'Then they don't know Kate,' Dee told him icily. 'If there was one female in this place who wouldn't even consider an affair, it's her. She can't stand being touched.'

There was a thick silence. Slowly Eliot said: 'What do you mean?'

'Her husband was a sadist and he got his kicks hurting her. Kate would throw up if a man came too close to her again.'

She was shivering, her eyes closed now, hearing it all and half hysterical. 'No, no,' she tried to mumble, but her lips felt huge and swollen as if they were made of rubber, they couldn't even part to let the words out. She couldn't stand hearing Dee saying those things. She did not want Eliot Holman to know all that. Dee had no right to repeat things she had said to him in confidence. He had no right.

'No right,' she muttered hoarsely.

It was true, but put so bluntly, with such terse flat understanding, it hurt more than ever. Toby had enjoyed hurting her. Had she told Dee that? Or had he guessed? She had skated over the surface when they talked about it, but had some glimpses of the hell she had been through during her marriage come home to him? You might read of such things happening to other women, but you did not expect it to happen to you, and in the polite, smiling social world there was pressure to make you keep such things to yourself. People did not want to see the barbaric faces which a mask can hide. Her father had made light of her first, weeping outcry. A lovers' quarrel, he had smiled. That's all it is, Kate.

'Don't tell me you've never kissed her,' Eliot said with a rasp. 'The day she overheard us talking in your office, I was outside, remember? I heard you kiss her then. Don't tell me I imagined it. I didn't see you, but then I didn't need to. It was obvious.'

'Oh, hell,' Dee muttered.

'Don't lie to me,' Eliot threw back.

'I'm not. Yes, I kissed her then—I was in a mood to hit someone and Kate annoyed me. It was a rotten thing to do. She hated it. You didn't see her face.'

'I did,' Eliot said slowly. 'She looked livid, but I thought that was over the job.'

Dee shifted his feet restlessly and Kate stared at them with bright feverish eyes, trying to gather the energy to stand up and stop this before she passed out. They shouldn't be talking about her like this— she wouldn't have it. How dared they put her under a microscope as if she were a performing flea? They were ignoring her, discussing her freely as if she were invisible. Did they think she couldn't hear them?

'What's wrong with her?' Dee asked, his voice closer. 'She looks as if she needs a doctor.'

'Judy is bringing the night nurse down. Where the hell are they? I sent Judy up a quarter of an hour ago. Surely it can't be taking this long to locate the damned woman?'

' 'Flu,' Kate said very loudly, pleased to find herself able to speak again.

'What?' Dee bent and she opened her eyes to look at him. He had a concerned frown. 'What did you say, Kate?'

'Don't,' she said but the rest of the sentence had slipped away. Don't talk about me, she thought, but the words didn't emerge.

Dee straightened. 'You see?' he said to Eliot. 'Get too close and she prickles like a hedgehog.'

'I thought it was me,' Eliot said oddly. 'I thought she just couldn't stand me.'

'She can't stand men of any shape or description,' Dee said with a long sigh. 'Bitter as hell about them.'

'When I first came everyone told me she was still pining for her husband.'

'She lets them think that because it keeps the other men at a distance. She admitted as much to me.'

There was another silence and Kate found herself sliding away into a remote trance which held a fevered comfort.

'He must have been a swine,' Eliot said.

'Yes.' Dee came closer again and brushed the dark hair back from Kate's hot forehead. 'And she's a tiny little thing. Men like that make me sick.'

'Tiny she may be, but she packs quite a punch,' Eliot muttered with a trace of amusement. 'Some days I'm reeling by the time I get out of here. This office turns into a boxing ring when she's in one of her tempers. My God, that girl has a temper! Tongue like a razor and eyes that can slice you into bits.'

'Self-protection,' Dee commented.

Kate did not care any more. They could say what they liked. She let their low voices fall away into the darkness and lapsed into a peaceful sleep.

Someone was touching her, lifting her wrist, cold fingers holding it for a moment. ''Flu,' someone said. 'Everyone's going down with it. She's got it badly. Bed and some aspirin.'

Other things were said. Kate heard Judy talking in a brisk, cold voice and wanted to look at her but couldn't lift her eyelids. Judy was cross with her.

Tears trickled from under her lids. That made her feel very sad.

'Are you all right, Kate?'

'Judy,' she whispered threadily.

'Yes?' Judy did not sound quite so sharp now.

'Not true,' Kate muttered.

'Just relax,' Judy said quite kindly.

Something was happening. Kate forced her heavy lids open and saw lights swaying overhead, walls passing. With a frown she made herself focus on a face close above her own and found Eliot watching her.

'Where?' she mumbled.

'I'm taking you home. Don't worry, Judy is with us.' He sounded calm and remote, a stranger.

'Judy.' Her frown deepened and it hurt. It hurt to think. She knew she had to force herself to concentrate, but when she did her head hurt so badly that she had to close her eyes again and slip back into the comfortable darkness.

During the night she woke up with a raging thirst, her whole body burning with heat. The room was dark. She groped across the bedside table to the lamp and something crashed to the floor. The door flew open and light fell across her flushed face.

'Judy?' Kate frowned. 'What are you doing here?' She remembered now and was pleased to find her voice quite normal.

'I stayed to make sure you were all right,' Judy said, coming across to switch on the lamp. She picked up the clock and replaced it. 'Are you O.K.? Anything I can get you?'

'A drink, please. I'm dying of thirst.'

'You would be,' Judy agreed, and poured some water

from a jug by the bed. 'I put this here for you in case. You've slept well. It's four o'clock—you've been asleep since nine last night.'

'It's 'flu, isn't it? I suppose I should have expected it. Half the staff have gone down with it.' Kate held the glass in both hands and drained it greedily. The water put new life into her. Judy filled the glass again.

'Want some more?'

Kate shook her head, lying back.

'Think you can sleep again?'

'Judy.' She struggled to find the words. 'Thanks for staying.' That was easy, but she had something else she had to say.

'Forget it.' Judy switched off the light.

'Who's looking after Kevin?'

Judy paused at the door, looking back at her. 'Dee.'

That sounded hopeful. Kate closed her eyes, smiling. 'Good.'

When she woke up again it was a golden sunlight filling the room. She drank a second glass of water and lay with closed eyes, still so hot the sheets burnt with the emanation of her body. She felt like something sizzling on a griddle. After a while she had some more water and then she fell into a restless doze again.

She woke again because her temperature had broken and sweat was pouring from her body, soaking the sheets and making her shiver.

Judy changed the sheets and changed her nightdress. 'You're being very kind,' Kate whispered. 'Sorry to be such a nuisance.'

'You're not a nuisance. You can do the same for me some day. How do you feel?'

'Fine,' she said.

Judy laughed. 'What a liar you are!'

'No, really. Much better.' She felt cool and alive again, her body back to normal, slightly cold if anything. Judy had gently passed a cool, damp flannel over her face and hands. The nightdress felt deliciously fresh on her limbs and her head was working clearly. She looked at Judy, hesitating.

'Judy, nothing's going on between me and Dee.'

'I know.' Judy gave her a brief, dry smile. 'Eliot told me.'

How much else had he told her? Kate remembered the weird, dislocated conversation the two men had had the night before. She felt her face flaming. How could they? Her teeth clamped together. The nerve of it, talking about her right there in front of her!

She pushed her own problems aside. She would think about that later. Looking at Judy's cool smile she said gently: 'Dee loves you very much, you know.'

'He's got a funny way of showing it.' Judy was a practical, clear-minded woman, but her voice was stiff with pain and anger as she spoke. Kate looked at her closely and realised more than ever that Judy was going through a bad time. Her usual warmth and liveliness had been wiped out and her face was set in cold lines.

Kate had known her for some time, but they had not been really close friends. All she knew of Judy was the friendly smile she had always got until Judy began to believe that Kate was seeing Dee.

'He does, Judy,' she insisted quietly.

'Do you want to know why I found it so easy to believe that you and he were making it?' Judy's colour had rushed up, her eyes wide with pain. 'It's happened before. So don't tell me, Kate, that he loves me. If he did, he wouldn't have other women.'

'But are you sure he has?' Kate still didn't believe it. Dee's feelings about his wife did not fit this story. Or were all men liars and opportunists?

'I'm sure.' Judy said that bitterly. 'While I was in the States Eliot threw a party for me and this girl came. She was Dee's secretary a few years back. She got a bit drunk and blurted it all out. She cried all over me, said she hated herself but Dee had talked her into bed, and she had left to get away from him.' Judy gave Kate a tight little smile. 'Patty Hare wasn't the first or the last, but she's the one I actually know about.'

Kate frowned. 'What did Dee say?'

'You don't think I asked him?' Judy moved restlessly. 'From what that girl told me, it had been going on for years. She said he was notorious. He tested all his secretaries.'

'I don't believe it!' Kate half sat up. 'Judy, you work on the paper. How could he hide it from you?'

'The wife's always the last to know,' Judy said icily. She looked down at her hands, spread them as though they fascinated her. 'Kate, Patty Hare was a ravishing little blonde of twenty-three. I'm thirty-six and I'm no knockout.'

Kate watched her, following her train of thought. 'You half expected it, didn't you?'

Judy smiled bitterly. 'Dee has always got a second look from women. When I first met him he had a positive trainload of them hanging around.'

Had Judy always been jealous? Kate wondered, frowning. What did she know about her, anyway?

What does one know of anyone? What people say isn't always a good clue to what they think.

'You're hardly without your own attraction,' she suggested, watching Judy. 'Eliot seems to find you irresistible.'

Judy grimaced with a wry amusement. 'He told me that Dee thought we were having an affair. No, Kate, Eliot's an old friend, a good friend, but we aren't sleeping together.'

'Maybe he'd like it to be otherwise,' said Kate.

Judy glanced at her. 'You sound just the tiniest bit jealous.'

Kate felt her colour rush from every corner of her body. She stiffened furiously, her eyes widening. 'You've got to be joking! I can't stand the sight of him.'

Judy shrugged. 'All right, I imagined it.' She stood up. 'Would you be able to eat anything?'

Kate closed her eyes. 'No, thank you, I'm fine. I don't want to keep you from work, Judy. It's very kind of you, but please, don't bother to stay. I'm fine now.'

'Just go back to sleep,' said Judy, going out.

Sleep was much easier now and Kate felt cool and free as she let it wash back over her. She opened her eyes later to find the light had shifted round the room. When she looked at the clock she was amazed to see that she had slept for another six hours. Her stomach gave a pang at the realisation. She was hungry now. She carefully pushed back the covers and stood up, swaying slightly. Funny, she felt as though she had been in bed for a hundred years. Her legs were rubbery and her body shivered as she stood up. Slowly she made her way to the bathroom and came out again, her face refreshed after a dash of lukewarm water.

'What are you doing out of bed?' demanded Judy.

She smiled at her. 'Testing my legs.'

'And how are they?'

'Working again.'

'How's your appetite?'

'Ravenous,' Kate laughed. 'I really do feel normal again.'

'It passes off quickly,' Judy agreed. 'Tomorrow you'll be as fit as a fiddle.'

She guided Kate back to the bedroom and drew the covers over her. 'What would you like? How about an omelette?'

'Sounds heavenly,' Kate sighed, getting hungrier.

It was light and golden, a perfect semi-circle, and as she ate it Kate said lightly, 'Dee is sick of eating out of tins. He misses your cooking.'

'I'm weeping,' Judy said with savagery.

'Talk to him,' Kate pleaded. 'Ask him, Judy. Let him have a chance to clear himself.'

'Why should I?' Judy got up and walked to the door. 'I'll never forgive him. I could have stood it if he hadn't hidden it from me, but it makes a mockery of our whole marriage. If he lied once, he might have lied a dozen times. How many others have there been? Dee's an attractive man. I know other women find him interesting. Do you think I haven't seen them looking at him? I thought he loved me, I thought I could trust him. Well, I'll never trust him again!'

The door slammed and Kate stared at it with a disturbed, distressed face. She could understand Judy's violence, her pain, her anger, but she remembered Dee's bitter jealousy of Eliot and she just did not believe that he had been unfaithful to Judy. Dee had always impressed her as a man who could keep his hands to himself. He had kissed her once, but it had been a punishment, a gesture of rage; there had been no sensual interest in it at all. It hadn't made her sick the way Eliot had because under Eliot's forceful kisses she had felt something quite different. She put her hands to her hot face. As Eliot held her down she had known he wanted her. She had felt it. She had not felt anything of the kind in Dee's arms. Her anger with him had been because she had recognised clearly the sexual humiliation he was inflicting—Dee had had no desire for her at all, merely a furious wish to inflict a defeat on her. He could have hit her, he could have bawled her out. Instead he had done what he had known instinctively would sting worse—he had treated her as a woman, but with cold, barbaric rage, not desire.

Judy came back later to remove her plate. 'Want anything else?' she asked. 'Another drink?'

Kate shook her head. 'I'm really very grateful to you for being so kind,' she started, and Judy made a brusque gesture.

'Forget it.' She turned her head as the doorbell chimed. 'I expect that's Eliot.'

'Eliot?' Kate sat up, trembling. 'I don't want him here.'

'Grateful little darling, aren't you?' Judy asked with amusement. 'He carried you down to the car and then carried you in here—a perfect gentleman, too. Cleared off as soon as he'd dumped you on the bed. Some men would have stayed to enjoy the sight of you being stripped.'

Kate glared at her. 'Very funny!'

Judy grimaced. 'No, it wasn't, was it? Sorry.' She went out and Kate tensely listened to the sound of voices. It was not Eliot's voice, she realised suddenly. It was Dee's.

The door opened. 'It's Dee,' Judy anounced in a cold sharp voice. 'Do you want to see him?'

'Yes, please,' said Kate, and watched Judy's eyes.

Dee walked in with a face wreathed in smiles, but Kate could see that it was all a surface enjoyment. Dee's hazel eyes were like knives.

'How are you, Kate my love?' he asked, and bent to kiss her.

Judy slammed the door.

Kate eyed him drily. 'You like to dig your own grave, don't you?'

He sat on the edge of the bed with a sullen expression. 'I'm not waiting for her to do it.'

'Dee, have you ever had an affair with anyone?' she asked suddenly.

He looked at her quickly, oddly. There was a long pause. 'Are you propositioning me?' he asked with a strange intonation.

'No. Leave me out of it. In the past, Dee, have you ever had an affair?'

'No, but I can't say the same for the future,' he muttered.

'Be serious, Dee!'

'I am,' he said grimly. 'The next little blonde I see, I promise you.'

'What about a girl called Patty?'

Dee's head swung. 'What?'

Kate looked into his eyes. 'She was a blonde, wasn't she?'

Dee frowned and said slowly, 'Patty was, yes. She was with me for about six months and it took us a year to sort out the mess she'd made of everything. The worst secretary I ever had.'

'What else?' Kate asked drily.

'What are you talking about?' He stared at her with his brows knitted. 'What is all this?'

'While Judy was in the States she met Patty at a party and Patty told her that she'd been your mistress.'

'What?' Dee was off the bed, tense as an animal, his face shaken and angry. 'You're kidding!'

'No.'

He stared at her, looked at the door. 'Judy never breathed a word to me, not a bloody syllable. She believed it?'

'She said Patty was a ravishing little blonde of twenty-three.' Kate eyed him. 'Of course she believed it.'

'Why didn't she say something, ask me? Why just turn off me without a damned word? My God ...' He was wordless, his face dangerous. 'I'll kill her,' he said. 'I'll choke her until she can't speak.' Dark red flooded up to his hairline. 'Eliot,' he said thickly. 'Tit for tat, was that it?' She heard him swallow. 'I'll kill her! My God, how could she be so stupid?'

Kate did not need to ask if it was true. She could see it in his face. Dee was red and then white. He was moving restlessly, his hands clenched at his sides. The hazel eyes were glittering with temper.

'That spiteful little bitch,' he muttered. 'She had it in for me because I sacked her, I suppose.' He snarled.

'If I ever set eyes on her again I'll slap her head off!'

Watching him Kate wondered if Patty's spite had been purely inspired by having been sacked. Judy was right; Dee was an attractive man. Maybe Patty had fancied him and been livid because he had never even looked at her. A woman scorned, she thought, half smiling.

'Don't tell me,' she advised with amusement. 'Tell Judy.'

'Tell her?' Dee moved to the door with a rapid, tense stride. 'I'm going to take the truth and stuff it down her stupid throat!'

As he flung open the door Judy appeared, a tray of coffee in her hand. Kate could not see Dee's face—his back was towards her. But she could see Judy's and she watched alarm and surprise come into it as she stared at Dee.

The back of his neck was brick red. 'I want a word with you,' he said very softly, and the whole set of his body shouted danger.

'Well, I don't want to talk to you,' Judy began aggressively, and Dee snatched the tray from her, the cups rattling, and flung it down on to a table near the door. He grabbed Judy's arm in a whirling movement and shoved her out of the room. The door slammed behind them.

'Get your hands ...' Judy began outside, and the words stopped dead. After a long moment Kate heard her say huskily, 'You swine,' and then there were struggling movements and footsteps. A door slammed elsewhere in the apartment and Kate heard no more. Sliding out of bed, she got herself a cup of coffee and waited.

CHAPTER SEVEN

DEE put his head round the door half an hour later and gave Kate a hard, exalted grin. 'I'm going now. Get well soon—we miss you!' He did not wait to say more, waved and vanished. She heard him leaving, and then Judy came back, very flushed, her eyes over-bright with what Kate suspected were shed tears, but smiling. She looked across the room and Kate smiled at her.

'You were right,' Judy said, laughing unsteadily. 'And I'm a stupid, credulous idiot. I have that on the best authority.'

'Beat you, did he?'

'I'm lucky to be alive,' said Judy, mouth curving. Her face sobered. 'Kate, what stupidity! Eighteen months of hell and all for a lying, vicious little bitch like that! Dee's right—I am a fool.' She paused, drawing a hard breath. 'If I ever meet her again! My God, how she must have laughed when she heard about the divorce!'

'Hell hath no fury,' Kate murmured.

'Oh, obviously,' Judy seethed. 'She had an eye on him and Dee never even noticed.'

'I told you he'd never struck me as that sort of man,' Kate said. 'I've never heard a whisper about him. And if there had been one it would have got to me sooner or later.'

Judy sat down on the bed and made a wry face. 'I was ripe for it, though, Kate. I realise that now.'

'How do you mean?'

'Going over to the States made me feel my age. I was on my own and God! I felt lonely. I missed Dee.' She paused. 'I suppose I've always felt faintly afraid I'd lose him one day. I never was a raving beauty. And when that girl told me her lies I believed them because I was half inclined to be afraid of something like that.'

Kate made a fist and poked her with it lightly. 'If you'd seen Dee grinding his teeth because he thought Eliot was your lover, you wouldn't lose any sleep over losing Dee. He's nuts about you.'

Judy flushed and laughed, looking away. 'Let's celebrate,' she said lightly. 'How about a cup of tea?'

'Doesn't this rate champagne?'

'Have you got any?' Judy asked with surprise.

'No,' said Kate, laughing. 'So it will have to be tea.' She had drunk two cups of coffee, but she could see Judy needed to do something. When women were either miserable or joyful they always needed to be busy, to work out the emotions which men expressed in other ways.

Judy went back to look after her home and son next day and Kate went home to her parents. Dee drove her, whistling happily all the way. 'Take as long as you like,' he told her as he left her. 'Eliot can manage.'

'Are you sure?' she had frowned.

'You did,' Dee pointed out drily. 'But then you're superhuman, we all know that. All five foot three of you.'

'Sarcasm,' she retorted. 'That's not nice to an invalid.'

'Some invalid,' Dee grinned. 'A tank would back away, Kate my love. You are a very impressive lady.'

Kate was not sure she liked being compared to a tank. 'I'm a frail little female,' she told him firmly.

Dee shouted with laughter. 'Frail? Is that how you see yourself? Eliot Holman wouldn't agree with you. He's still limping from the last time you kicked him to his knees.'

Kate glared after him as he went, still laughing. She didn't think that was funny. Her father saw Dee out and came in to eye her with concern. 'You're washed out, Katie. You must have had the 'flu badly.'

'It wasn't a picnic,' she agreed.

'You're not as strong as you think you are,' he said, and she looked at him wrathfully. Not another one! What was this? A conspiracy to convince her she was a delicate little flower unfit for the tough, strong world of men? Her father was looking at her with wry affection. 'I know you sometimes give the impression of being made of steel wire, but you're flesh and blood like the rest of us, Katie.'

'Who said I wasn't?' She stirred belligerently, looking at him with sparkling eyes. 'I'm human,' she said, in the voice of one who would dearly love to dispute it.

He patted her cheek. 'And lovely with it,' he said, smiling.

The next day she lay in a lounger in the garden while Oliver tiptoed around like someone in the presence of mortality, fetching cushions, making coffee. 'Don't be saintly,' she begged. 'My nerves are too weak.'

'Sweet little sister,' he said in a honeyed voice. 'Always so gentle and loving.'

Kate grinned. 'O.K., how much is it going to cost me?'

He gave her a wounded look, sniffing. 'There's no need to be vicious. Can't I bring you coffee without being accused of bribery?' He sat down on the grass beside her chair and propped himself up with both hands, his untidy dark head thrown back. 'It's nice to have you home again for a few days, that's all. I miss you now and then.'

'Touching,' Kate said drily.

Oliver's blue eyes stayed on her face. 'You were more fun when I was a kid. Marriage didn't suit you, Kate.'

She looked at the bright blue sky. 'No.' That was the understatement of the year, God knew.

'I never cared much for him,' Oliver murmured, watching her. 'He smiled too much and stopped when nobody was looking.'

Kate's head moved sharply. She stared at his serious young face. 'Perceptive of you.'

He nodded, half smiling. 'Mum thinks your heart's broken.'

Kate sighed. 'Yes, I know.'

Oliver got up, smiling at her. 'Drink your coffee before it gets cold.'

She sipped. It was vile. 'What did you put in it? Arsenic?'

'Brandy,' Oliver said complacently. 'Buck you up.'

When he had gone she poured it all into the grass, hoping it wouldn't shrivel it at the roots. Dad was devoted to his carefully manicured lawns. But she wasn't drinking that stuff.

She lay back, her head delightfully cushioned, the lounge chair taking all her weight, letting the sun sink into her flesh and careful to keep her head covered as instructed by Dr Marchant under the fringed yellow umbrella he had fixed to her chair. 'No more sun-stroke,' he had warned her.

An hour later she still lay there, the book she had been pretending to read face down on the grass, her hand dangling from the arm of the chair. A movement brought her out of the light doze and she opened her eyes.

'Oh,' she said, taken aback. 'Hello.'

She felt ludicrously at a disadvantage. Eliot towered over her, his fair head gleaming smoothly in the sunshine. He was dressed. Kate was in her briefest bikini and felt naked.

'How are you?' he asked.

There was a peculiar uneasiness between them. The last time they met had been a highly charged experience. She shivered slightly, recalling the talk she had overheard between him and Dee. The realisation that Eliot now knew so much about her made her feel silly and prickly.

'I'm fine,' she answered him politely, distantly.

'Good.' He sounded as off balance as she felt, an uncertainty in his face.

He glanced round the garden. 'Pretty,' he commented.

'Yes. My father's pride and joy.'

'Not you?' He wasn't looking at her. 'Aren't you his pride and joy?'

She wasn't sure how to take that. As sarcasm? Or was he being lightly funny? 'Oh, me too,' she said in a brittle tone. 'He dotes on me.'

'I'm sure he does.'

A peculiar conversation, Kate thought, staring at his

averted head. In profile his face looked tougher, sharper, less charming. It gave a better reflection of the man behind that smooth mask.

She bent to pick up her book and he turned and stooped to get it for her, putting it into her hand. Kate thanked him briefly, looking at it rather than him, then looked up to find his eyes wandering over her in a way which brought colour rushing into her face.

She was a slender girl, fine-boned and slightly built, the brevity of her bikini giving him an unobstructed view of the small, high breasts, the tiny waist, the pale gold of her flat stomach.

His eyes lifted to her face, skimmed it. 'I can look, can't I?' he asked aggressively.

'I wasn't expecting company.'

'I called in to see how you were and bring messages from everyone. Mirry is very worried about you.'

Kate laughed and after a quick look Eliot laughed too. 'Well, that's what she said,' he expanded, his eyes bright.

Mirry and Kate were hardly bosom friends, but Mirry did have a sentimental streak under her sulky manner. 'Give her my love back,' Kate told him. 'Thank you for calling.'

His face took on sarcasm. 'Thanks, but goodbye?'

She looked away. 'I didn't mean to sound rude.'

'You do it without trying. I've never been slapped down so often in my life.'

She made a wry gesture at herself. 'I'm in no condition to slap anybody down right now.'

He looked at her oddly. 'Not even if I provoke you?'

'Are you going to?'

His eyes glinted and his face changed. 'I think I

am,' he said, and swooped quickly.

The kiss brushed her mouth so softly it was like the touch of a feather and gone before she could react. He straightened but stayed with both hands gripping the arms of her lounger, looking at her mockingly. 'Well,' he whispered, 'hit me.'

Something weird was happening to her heartbeat and she couldn't hold his stare. She looked away. 'Not today,' she said as lightly as she could. 'Try some other time.'

'Oh, I will,' he promised.

She looked back at him, stirring half angrily, but he was looking down her slender relaxed body again and the half-sheathed eyes were a vivid blue. They took their time and Kate moved uneasily, feeling almost as if he was touching her. The intent, fascinated way he was staring made her hot from head to foot.

He looked back at her face. 'Beautiful,' he said very softly. 'There's not much of you, but what there is is enchanting.'

'I've told you before, I don't like men who flirt.'

He sat down beside her chair and put his hands round his knees, his chin on his hands. 'Who's flirting?'

'You're not?' Her dry tone made him smile, a sideways twist of the mouth which was self-derisive.

'Oh, no,' he said. 'Don't you know the difference? I fancied you the minute I saw you and it seems like months ago, not just weeks. Why do you think I was so mad over what I thought was going on between you and Dee? I was as jealous as hell.'

Kate's mouth went dry. She stared at her own hands holding the book. 'Please ...' she began, and he cut her off.

'I know—Dee told me. You hate men because your husband was a brute.'

'He had no right to tell you. I told him in strict confidence.'

'Well, he did tell me. Was that why you were sick when I kissed you?'

She didn't answer. There was a little silence. The sun poured down and there was a joyful thrush somewhere in the garden, singing at the top of his voice.

'I thought you hated me so much you couldn't stand having me touch you,' Eliot said lightly.

'It wasn't personal.' Kate made herself speak, but the words were thin and dry. 'It would have been the same with anyone.'

'You weren't sick just now,' he said in a soft warm voice.

Kate looked at him guardedly. 'That wasn't the same.'

'No,' he agreed, smiling at her. 'But then last time I was half crazy with jealousy.'

She looked away hurriedly, trembling.

'I won't hurry you,' Eliot said huskily. 'But when you're better will you have dinner with me?'

Kate felt a restless uneasiness inside her, a curious fluttering, as though her heart had begun to beat twice as fast. Eliot knelt up and moved his head so that his face was close to her own, his eyes watching her. He touched her cheek with one long finger. It felt cool against her sunheated skin. 'I fancy you,' he whispered. 'But you know that, don't you? You're a very pretty girl and we could have a lot going for us, Kate.'

The sun outlined his head and turned his face into a golden mask; deceptive, far too attractive. Under the smooth skin she saw the hard bones which gave away the iron nature under the charm. His mouth was warm, sensual, curving in a faint smile.

'I realise you're afraid of getting hurt again,' he told her gently. 'Trust me, Kate. I won't hurt you, I won't ask you for more than you feel you can give for the moment.'

His mouth was moving closer and she knew he was going to kiss her again. She turned her head aside, shaking it. 'Don't, please.'

He knelt there, watching her. After a moment he said, 'All right.' He touched her cheek again with that finger. 'All right, Kate, I'll wait.' He stood up. 'I'll see you back at the office, then. But think about it, Kate. Give me a chance to show you it could be different this time.'

She had plenty of time to think during the time she spent at home. She had resisted Eliot's advances, but she had to face the fact that she had not been unaware of him even while she did so—she had wanted to give in when he tried to kiss her. She had been frightened, but she had felt responsive, all right. That frightened her even more. She did not want to feel like that. It undermined her determination.

When she went back to the office Mirry was very nice to her and Kate responded by being very sweet-tempered all that first day, aware that Mirry was leaning over backwards not to provoke her into one of her sharp moods. I've turned into a bitch, Kate thought, wry and self-mocking. Mirry's careful behaviour showed her just how alarming she had become without realising it. Sometimes Mirry drove her to it—would drive a saint into a temper. But sometimes Kate knew she had just been difficult and barbed from sheer habit.

Eliot took the day off as she was back. Kate was able to slide back into the routine without having him around to distract her. When he did come back they fell into a calm working pattern which had none of the scratchy irritations of the period before her illness.

'You were worn out,' Judy told her. 'Too much work and too much tension. Something had to give.'

Kate had been regaled with the office gossip about Dee and Judy, but she had had a pared-down version because people still weren't sure how close she had been to Dee and they walked warily in case they were treading on her dreams. They would forget it all in time and Kate's back was broad enough to take the sideways glances and discreet curiosity.

She had forgotten all about the French trip and when Eliot brought it up she looked at him with hurriedly disguised shock. She did not want to go away with him for several days. She was nervous of the possible intimacy of that situation. 'Maybe you should go alone this time,' she suggested.

He gave her a sharp look. 'It's all set up,' he insisted. The grey eyes coldly observed her nervous expression and one of his brows lifted in sardonic comment. 'Too bad if you don't think you can stand my company that long. It's only work, remember.'

She flushed. 'I didn't . . .'

'Oh, yes,' he drawled, 'you did. Those big blue eyes looked like a frightened rabbit's. And don't jump every time I come anywhere near you. It gets on my nerves.'

'I don't jump.'

'You do,' he said flatly. 'Six foot in the air. I'm not suddenly going to pounce on you and devour you.'

'I didn't think you were!'

'No?' He smiled unpleasantly. 'Sure?'

Kate stared at him with a flushed face and sparking eyes. 'Do we have to have this sort of thing? Can't you work with someone without dragging sex into it all the time?'

'What would you know about sex, you frigid little icicle?' he asked her with a cool stare. 'If I ever drag it in you can be sure you'll know all about it.'

'Just try!' Kate burst out, seeing the derision in his eyes with rage.

'Oh, I will,' he murmured drily. 'But you can wait for it.' He gave her a sidelong smile, his lashes covering his eyes. 'It will do you good.'

She was so annoyed that she would have hit him if he hadn't caught her hand as it swung upwards, forcing her arm down by her side and holding it there in a light but unbreakable grip which annoyed her even more by the effortless ease with which he controlled her.

'I am not going to France with you,' she promised him, turning the angry glare of her blue eyes on to his smiling face, hating the unhidden amusement he showed her.

'Oh, yes, you are,' he assured her.

'You can't force me to go.'

'You work for me, remember? And who's dragging sex into it, you or me? We're going there to do a story, not so that I can gratify my lust for your delectable little body.'

'You ...' She was speechless, raging at the insolent way he had said that, looked at her as he said it.

He began to laugh at her incoherent fury. 'What's

the matter? Don't you like the truth?' He lowered his voice, whispering teasingly. 'It is delectable, Kate. Especially in a bikini.' He released her and moved away, his face returning to a cool mask. 'But we're going to France on business. We'll have a photographer with us. I think Steve Martin's been assigned.'

The day they flew to Paris it was so hot that the tarmac at the airport was melting and cracking open in the sun. Steve Martin was a thickset young man with a gloomy face. He stared out of the window. 'I hope we're going to get safely off the ground.'

'Optimist,' Eliot drawled. He glanced at Kate's cold, averted face. 'A sunny pair I'm landed with,' he sighed. Kate ignored him and Steve opened a glossy trade magazine to become absorbed in detailed discussions on lenses and technical tricks.

Their flight was perfectly uneventful, as it happened, and when they got to their hotel the foyer was packed with people trying to reach the reception desk. 'Hell's bells,' Steve grumbled. 'Charming! We're going to have to wait all day to sign in, I see that.'

'I'll see to it,' Kate offered. 'No need for all of us to wait.'

'Sure?' Steve needed little persuasion. 'I could do with a drink. Coming, Eliot?'

Eliot shrugged. 'Too tired,' he said. 'You go, Steve.'

Steve glanced from him to Kate and grinned. 'I get you.'

When he had gone Kate turned her shoulder towards Eliot and ignored him. She hadn't liked the way Steve grinned. Eliot wandered away and inspected the foyer. She saw him eyeing a tall, willowy blonde in a dark dress who gave him a quick, interested look in return. Kate looked in the other direction. The shuffle to the reception desk took half an hour and by the time she had got there she was doubly tired and very cross. The girl behind the counter was cross too. They snapped at each other politely while the usual forms were filled out and the keys were bestowed.

Eliot took the keys and glanced at the numbers. He handed one back to her and kept the other two. They had agreed to meet Steve in the foyer some hours later. Kate said nothing in the elevator and parted from Eliot wordlessly in the corridor outside her room. He went into the next room. She had expected that. She looked out of the window and saw that she was looking out on to an airless little brick well from which she could see only the windows on the other side of the hotel. Below came the revving of a van and shouted imprecations in French that told her the kitchen was underneath her room some floors down.

She opened the windows wide but the hot, stale room remained intolerable. It was like an oven. The narrow bed, pale gold wardrobe and matching chest of drawers and dressing-table, the television and telephone might be called furnishing, but it could not turn the dull little box into a pleasant room. She took a cool shower and slid into a thin cotton dress, feeling slightly more human.

Eliot tapped on the door, surprising her by having brought up some French papers. 'We can do some homework while we eat,' he told her.

'I'm not hungry,' she said. 'Thirsty, but not hungry.'

'It's too hot,' he agreed. He glanced over her, awaking pulses she had thought would sleep for ever. 'You look cool, anyway.'

He closed the door and she backed, alarm in her face. 'We could have a drink in the bar,' she said huskily.

He moved towards her.

'Don't,' she said lamely, astonished to find herself looking at his mouth and not backing away.

'I want a few words with you,' Eliot bit out, astonishing her even further because the cold tone of his voice showed her that what she had imagined was on his mind could not be further from the truth. All the excitement which had come flooding into her veins had been fuelled by her own feelings, not his, and that shook her.

'I didn't like the way you acted on the way over here,' he told her crisply. 'You and I have to work together for the next few days with Steve Martin watching us, and I don't want you treating me with icy disdain in front of him. Do you understand?'

'Don't shout at me!' Kate said furiously, feeling a fool because she had misunderstood his intentions.

'Listen,' said Eliot between his teeth, 'one day you and I are going to have a nasty row, lady, if you don't moderate your tone when you talk to me.'

The grey eyes were little bits of sparkling ice as he stared at her. Kate stared back, her jaw aggressive.

'You think you frighten me, don't you?' she spat back like an infuriated kitten, her whole slender body quivering with temper. 'Well, you don't. I'll talk to you how I like.'

'Will you?' he asked softly, dangerously. 'I'm trying to keep my temper, but you would try the patience of a saint.'

'Well, you're certainly no saint!'

'No,' he said hoarsely. 'So I don't see why I should behave like one.'

His hands shot out and dragged her towards him. Kate was astonished to feel a peculiar sensation of satisfaction deep inside herself. She had been snapping back at him, but all the time her mind had been set on other things and now she admitted it to herself, staring at his mouth, waiting with a fast-beating heart to feel the hard, sensual lips moving against her own. She wanted it to happen. Her heart was going so fast her ears were filled with drumming. She heard Eliot's breath catch, the icy look fading from his frowning face. His hands slid from her arms, moved down to encircle her waist. She felt his grey eyes probing her own for reaction and couldn't meet their stare. Her lids closed, she began to tremble.

His mouth slowly opened her lips, their exploration sensuous, unhurried, moving warmly and without pressure, teasing her lips to respond, brushing lightly and going away only to come back. Kate arched against him, aware of an odd boneless weakness in her body, a melting sweetness which grew as his hands moved passionately over her back, gripping her closer, pulling her nearer. Her hands were crushed between them and Kate involuntarily found herself slowly sliding them upwards, their fingertips discovering the contours of his body, the strong curves of his ribcage with that rapid-beating heart hidden within it. She ran her hands sensitively over his neck until they were buried in his hair, pressing through the warm strands to find the bone structure of his skull.

She was so absorbed in her own sensations that she did not realise that he was gently manoeuvring her

on to the bed and then she gave a muffled cry of panic.
'No!'

'Don't be frightened,' he muttered thickly, kissing
her neck just below her ear. 'I won't hurt you.'

'I can't,' she gasped, struggling against the sudden
awareness of what would happen if she did not stop
this now.

'Kate,' he whispered in an unsteady voice, 'don't
fight me, I won't go too fast for you, I promise.' His
mouth was brushing her skin lightly and she could
feel the tension in him. She recognised it because she
felt it herself and she didn't want to feel like that.

'I hate it,' she moaned wildly. 'I hate you—let me
go!'

She had her eyes open now and so she saw the dark
red colour come up into his face, the flare in the grey
eyes. 'What changed your mind?' he asked savagely.
'You wanted it just now.'

'No,' she lied, and knew she was lying. She had
wanted it, and from the fury in his eyes she knew that
he was perfectly aware she was lying. She had to make
him let her go. 'You make me sick!' she broke out,
using the nearest weapon.

It was a mistake. She knew that as she said it because
Eliot's face hardened, tautened, into a cruel white
mask. 'That's too bad,' he said hoarsely. 'That's really
tough, you little bitch, because you're just going to
have to be sick.'

The whole weight of his body held her down on to
the bed, he caught her head between his hands and his
mouth came down in a burning, savage cruelty, forcing hers open, forcing a hot intimacy on her which
refused to be denied, invading her mouth again and

again until she was mindless, yielding, as weak under the forcefully inflicted kiss as an addict in the grip of a narcotic.

When he lifted his head at last Kate lay there, shivering, drained, breathing in shallow gasps.

'Oh, hell,' Eliot muttered, staring at her. 'I'm sorry. God, I'm sorry. I didn't mean to do that.'

'Get out,' she mumbled through swollen painful lips. 'Get out of here!'

His temper flared again. 'What do you think I'm made of? I can't just turn on and off like a tap. You were driving me crazy, I thought you wanted me. When you said stop, something gave in my head.'

'What you mean is, I wasn't allowed to say stop—you can't allow me the common decency of a right to decide whether to go on or not. You have the physical edge over me, don't you? If you want it, I get it, like it or not.' The words poured thickly, bitterly out of her, her eyes on him in a glittering stare. 'Well, I don't like it, and I don't want it. So get out of here and never touch me again!'

He stared at her fixedly. 'He really was a first-class bastard, wasn't he?'

Kate drew a shaky breath. 'I don't want to talk about it.'

'No, I can see why.' He was frowning, his face hard. 'Have you ever talked about it? Why did you tell Dee?' He was staring at her. 'Why Dee?' His voice darkened. 'Are you in love with Dee?'

She moved irritably. 'No, I'm not. We just swapped horror stories.'

He grimaced. 'I see.' There was a little silence, then he said gently, 'Tell me, Kate.'

'You like horror stories, do you?' The barbed anger of her tone did not alter his sober face.

'I want to know what happened to you to make you like this,' Eliot quietly admitted.

Her contemptuous eyes observed him slowly. 'Oh, I think you have a pretty good idea, don't you? You and my late husband would have had a lot in common. He didn't take no for an answer, either, and his ways of deciding the issue weren't pleasant or easily forgettable. When he'd reduced me to doing whatever he demanded he would be quite charming. Put him in a good temper for days.'

Eliot swore under his breath. 'You think I'm like that? Thanks. Thanks a lot. My God, all men aren't cut on those lines.'

'I'm in no hurry to find out,' Kate said icily.

He got off the bed and pushed his hands down into his pockets. 'I need a drink,' he said tightly. 'Coming?'

'You go,' said Kate in a small thin voice. 'I'll be down later.'

He glanced at her in a brief frown, nodded and went out. Kate turned on to her face and burst into scalding tears.

CHAPTER EIGHT

BEFORE they left England Eliot had set up a series of interviews with people whose views of the current French situation he thought would be useful to them. They split the list in half, each taking an equal number of people. Eliot spent some time giving Kate a breakdown of what sort of thing he wanted and then the next day they went off around Paris to get their stories. Steve went with Eliot, since only two of the people rated pictures and both were on Eliot's list. They were both politicians, too, and to Kate's relief her list did not have any politicians on it. She had been given all the literary and artistic interviews. 'No sexual discrimination,' Eliot taunted with a brief grin, 'just common sense. You're too emotional for politics.'

'You're welcome to them,' she shrugged. 'I'll enjoy my work. I can't say the same for yours.'

'As I suspected,' he nodded.

Kate did enjoy her day. Although her French was comparatively good many of her interviewees turned out to be quite happy to speak in English and she was able to fill her pad with readable, interesting quotes. 'Just get my name right,' said one of them, giving her a typical Frenchman's sideways smile, knowledge-able, faintly flirtatious, admiring of her slender looks in the straight yellow sheath dress. 'Very chic,' he had already told her as he welcomed her to his office.

Steve bubbled with amusement about some pictures he had taken of Paris in the rush hour. 'Even worse than London,' he said.

'We may use one,' Eliot agreed.

Steve wandered away and Kate and Eliot glanced at each other. 'Good day?' he asked, and she shrugged. 'Not bad. And you?'

They were treating each other carefully, warily. What had happened last night hung between them like a spectre. Kate was incredibly nervous. When he glanced away from her she looked at him with new

eyes, seeing as if for the first time the hard gleaming
looks, the cool assurance he wore, the fair hair a smooth
cap above his strong features. He was wearing a casual,
open-necked shirt which left his throat bare and he
looked longer, leaner than she remembered, as though
he had grown. She had never stared at him as she was
staring now or been so deeply, hotly aware of him.

'Dinner?' he asked, glancing back, and she was furious with herself because she felt the red colour rushing into her face and knew he could see how stupidly
she was behaving.

'I want a shower first.' She was pleased to find her
voice steady, anyway.

'I'll see you down here in half an hour, then,' Eliot
suggested.

When they did meet they surveyed each other like
two duellists before a bout, their eyes guarded.

There was no sign of Steve and Eliot said with
amusement: 'He's gone off to look for more lively
entertainment. Paris has a lot of it to offer.'

She reacted like a scalded cat, her eyes flashing.
'Don't let me stop you finding it.' Oh, my God, she
thought, even as she said it, I'm jealous. Am I crazy?

Eliot turned a cool smile on her, his lips curling back
from his teeth in a barbed displeasure. 'Are you politely
giving me the brush-off?'

'We don't have to spend the whole evening together.'
She didn't know why she was talking to him like this
—it just kept coming out and in a minute he would
see through her set smile and catch sight of the jealous
anger underneath it.

'That's right,' he drawled icily. 'We don't. Why
didn't I think of that?' He closed a hand round her

arm, his fingers a vice, and thrust her like a naughty child towards the dining-room. 'Shall we eat?'

Her idiotic display had ruined the evening. They ate in a cold silence and afterwards she could not even remember what she had eaten. Towards the end of the meal a cabaret started. The first act was a girl singer in a tight red dress. Hor mournful song was crooned huskily into a mike, the dark hair and white clown's face making her comi-tragic.

Eliot drank brandy, his long legs crossed, a thin cigar smouldering and smoking in the shadows behind Kate's chair. She glanced round once, but he was watching the singer with apparent enjoyment. Kate felt restless. 'I think I'll go to bed,' she whispered as the applause lightly broke out. She got up and Eliot rose too. 'Stay and watch,' she said coolly, avoiding his eyes. 'Goodnight.'

Six stately scantily clad girls ran on to the small stage and Eliot flicked his eyes towards them. He sat down. 'Goodnight,' he said calmly.

In her room Kate paced up and down, fuming. She was angry with herself for that involuntary, unexpected reaction, and angry with Eliot for the amused appreciation in the grey eyes as those girls came into sight.

Flirt, she thought, gritting her teeth. And he was doing it deliberately. She had begun to recognise expressions on his face. He was clever, conscious of what he was doing. He was far too self-aware.

Lying in the darkness later she listened to the crashing sounds from the bottom of the brick well. The kitchen staff were quarrelling nastily in operatic French, shrieking insults at each other, and banging what sounded like metal trays together. She hoped

that wasn't going on all night. They had to leave for
Marseilles at a ridiculous hour of the morning. She
could not close the windows; the night was too hot.
She began to slide into sleep, only to be woken by a
voice in what sounded like demented Arabic wailing at
someone and, from the one-sided sound of it, talking
on the phone. A radio started somewhere and there
were televisions mumbling in other rooms. Kate
turned over and thumped her pillows. Her head was
aching and she could not sleep. She got out of bed and
padded into the bathroom to get some water. Getting
back into bed, she put the pillow over her head and
gradually managed to fall into an uneasy doze which
became real sleep as the night deepened and the temperature dropped slightly.

Her early call woke her from a heavy sleep. Half
an hour later, dark rings under her eyes, her temper
brittle, she made her way down to the foyer.

Eliot had set up a tight schedule, cramming into it
as much as he could in the time available. Steve was
bursting with energy this morning. Kate listened to
him telling Eliot what a great night he had had. 'Have
you had any sleep at all?' Eliot asked, and Steve
grinned as he shook his head. 'What do you run on?
Electricity?' Eliot demanded.

'Enjoy yourself, it's later than you think,' Steve retorted with an impish look.

'I hope she was worth it,' Eliot drawled. He hadn't
even looked at Kate this morning except to give a
curt nod.

'What about you?' asked Steve, sliding a sly look at
Kate.

She ignored him, turning over a French magazine

and reading the glossy advertisements without really seeing them.

'I worked in bed,' Eliot said, and Steve hooted with amusement.

'I bet!'

Kate walked away, stiff with fury. As they all got into the taxi which took them to the airport Eliot's hand brushed her knee and he took it away very obviously, a sidelong look pointing the fact.

Marseilles excited Steve almost as much as Paris. Eliot gave a few directions to him and then let him loose. 'So long as you bring back some good pictures you're on your own,' he assured him.

Eliot and Kate did the interviews this time—Kate watching with impressed interest as Eliot's fast gun-fire French rattled away in response to the answers he got. He had a clear idea of what he wanted to elicit, but he did not always go for it directly, she noted. He had an oblique method of drawing it out. His questions often sounded irrelevant and they came up with some very interesting answers. She watched him sum people up, change direction, let them talk freely or keep them within strict bounds according to the method he decided would prove most productive.

When they had done their last interview, he glanced at her and said: 'I know a beach not too many miles from here which won't be quite as crowded as the others. Want to try it?'

It was as hot as it had been in Paris, but the sea wind kept the air moving. She was tempted. 'That would be nice.'

'Don't sound so enthusiastic!'

'What do you want me to do?' she asked. 'Thank you on my knees?'

'A little warmth wouldn't come amiss,' Eliot told her curtly.

'If we're going to argue all the time, maybe you'd better go alone,' Kate snapped.

He stopped and looked down at her. 'A simple yes or no. Do you want to come or don't you?'

Pride warred with a desire for his company. She looked away and said crossly, 'Yes.'

He put a hand under her chin and made her look at him. 'Did that hurt?' he asked with dry amusement.

Flushed, she shook her head.

'Smile,' he whispered.

Her lips quivered. 'My God,' Eliot said mockingly, 'she's trying to smile.'

Kate laughed and pulled her head away. 'Swine!'

'Compliments embarrass me,' Eliot said complacently as he followed her.

He had hired a car for the day. The small red French car had a noisy engine but could get up quite a speed on the autoroutes. They made it to the beach faster than Eliot had anticipated. Kate bought a modest little swimsuit from a tourist shop near the sands and when she had changed into it in the public changing room she wandered out to find Eliot in brief black trunks staring out over the crowded beach.

He turned and inspected her, brow rising. 'Why so demure? I liked the bikini better.'

'That's why,' she retorted, trying not to stare at the long muscled hardness of his body. He was so much taller than her that her head only reached his shoulder as they walked down on to the sand. Her bare feet tingled from the heat coming up from the beach. She ran down to the blue water and waded into it, sucking in her breath as the coolness rose to her shoulders. Striking out, she swam steadily, hearing Eliot moving just out of eye range, keeping up with her without actually coming abreast. She turned over on to her back and floated, arms outstretched, staring back at the shoreline. White buildings danced in a sun haze. The small black figures on the beach had an antlike absorption.

'You swim well,' Eliot complimented her.

She turned her head and the sun struck into her eyes, framing his wet-darkened head in a glittering dazzle of light. 'So do you.'

'It's been a great summer.'

'Fantastic.'

It was safe when they kept to light small talk, impersonal topics on which they would not argue. Arguments flared into other things and Kate was too well aware that he wouldn't find it hard to make her think about those other things. Her mind might reject the danger of getting involved with him, but her body had other ideas.

As they swam back to the shore they ran into a group of young Frenchmen playing with a huge multi-coloured ball. It splashed down near Kate and she flung it back to them, getting an interested cheer from several who wouldn't mind pursuing other interests than ball-games. Eliot moved closer to her, his shoulder almost touching hers, and the young men shrugged.

Padding back up the hot beach, Kate stretched out on the towel they had managed to get from the shop where they had bought their bathing suits. Eliot stood beside her, his gaze wandering over her, and although she kept her eyes shut she knew what he was doing and her nerves prickled in reaction. She ran her fingers through her wet hair, winnowing it to help the drying process. The sun streamed down and her salted skin began to tingle with heat.

'Remember, you find the sun dangerous,' Eliot teased lightly, kneeling beside her. 'I'll get you some lotion.'

'No,' she said, but he had already risen and was striding away. Kate lay back with a sigh. She hated the thought of going back to the stuffy airless hotel room. The faint sea breeze moved over her skin in a light caress and the shouts and laughter of children came to her from all directions. Eyes closed, she dozed lightly, perfectly content.

When she felt the sand being kicked up by some-one's feet she opened her eyes and Eliot grinned at her. 'Lotus-eater!'

He had a huge cartwheel hat in one hand which he jammed on to her head, blanking out the sky. Kate laughed, pushing it back.

'Suits you,' he decided, considering her.

It was a brilliant scarlet straw, fringed at the brim, and it shaded her face deliciously. 'Thank you, that was very kind,' she said.

He knelt beside her, a large bottle in his hand. 'Now for a rescue operation,' he said lightly.

Kate stiffened, realising what he meant to do. 'No,' she said hastily. 'There's no need. The sun's going down.'

He gave an ironic glance up at the blue, blue sky.

'Oh? Given it its marching orders, have you? It doesn't seem to be taking much notice.'

The sun burnt steadily in that spotless, cloudless sky and Kate knew her excuse had been ridiculous. It was several hours to sunset and they both knew it.

'I wouldn't want your father to think I let you get sunstroke again,' Eliot told her silkily, unscrewing the lid and pouring lotion into his palm.

'I can do it myself.'

'You won't enjoy it as much as I will.' Eliot flicked her a teasing little smile. He lowered his voice. 'But you know that, don't you? I'm transparent to you, aren't I? Any excuse to get my hands on you.'

Her face was wearing two red spots now, little hot coins of temper and embarrassment. 'You think you're so funny!'

'In my situation I have little choice,' Eliot said drily. 'It's either laugh or cry, and I prefer the former.'

She was puzzled by the words, staring at him. What on earth was he talking about? Her bewilderment ended abruptly as he began to smooth the lotion into her bare shoulders, his hand moving in a slow caress along her sun-heated skin. Her heart gave a great leap. She lay watching him, her mouth going dry, trying to read his features and failing because they were coolly guarded, expressionless.

He ran his fingertips over her collarbone, down her arms and then taking more lotion began to rub it into her legs. Neither of them spoke and Kate slowly shut her eyes, perfectly aware that he was exploring her body deliberately, and not protesting. There were people all round them. She felt no panic or anger. She surrendered herself to the slow, stroking fingers and enjoyed what he was doing.

'Turn over,' he muttered.

She rolled over and lay with her arms flung out, her head turned sideways on the towel. Eliot picked up the hat which had fallen off as she turned and dropped it back on to her head. Kate laughed softly and felt him bend until his lips touched her cheek. The kiss was light, casual.

When he had finished and screwed up the bottle again he sat down beside her and they settled to sleep in the sun. Kate lost count of time. It was a blissful, relaxing experience.

When she heard Eliot move again she woke from the half-sleep she had fallen into and he touched her shoulder. 'I'm afraid we ought to be moving.'

She turned, sitting up, yawning. 'Must we?'

'We have another early start tomorrow, remember.'

'Bordeaux,' she said, regretfully.

'I'm afraid so.'

'Why not do the whole thing here?' she asked lightly. 'That would be fun. We could skip the rest of the interviews, make them all up, and spend the rest of the time just lying here in the sun.'

He flipped a lazy finger along the fringed brim of the sunhat. 'Don't tempt me.'

'Am I?' she asked, laughing, and saw his eyes glint abruptly.

'Oh, yes,' he whispered. 'Don't you know how lovely you are?'

Her gay mood changed at the look in his eyes. She glanced away, trembling. 'Don't.' She had been enjoying the leisurely peace of the afternoon, the sounds of the beach, the cry of gulls overhead, the laughter of the children and the soft whisper of the waves. Now her mood was shattered by the intrusion of the feeling in his eyes, that feeling which could so maddeningly arouse an answering echo inside herself.

'All right,' Eliot said slowly, 'I won't.'

He was angry now. He got up in a fast movement, his lean body hard and active, the long legs bloomed with salt and sand, their golden hair dusted with it. 'Coming?' he asked tightly.

Kate followed him, her throat hot with regret and dismay. They had achieved a sort of truce and now it had been wrecked by that brief clash. The sexual awareness between them ruined any chance they had of being in each other's company without friction. For a while today Kate had been able to forget the uneasy consciousness which had become a recurring factor between them, but now it was back, and she looked at his tall, striding figure with dark blue eyes.

They changed, met and drove back to Marseilles without more than a brief word or two. Eliot's sardonic eyes underlined the silence between them whenever he looked at her. They ate dinner at their hotel. Steve did not show up. 'Found himself a new niche,' Eliot commented drily. 'He'll be old before he's forty.'

'He seems to have bags of energy.'

Eliot's eyes held wicked amusement. 'He does.'

They were early going up to their rooms and had the elevator to themselves. It lurched as it stopped at their floor and Kate was flung forward. Eliot stopped her deftly and supported her. She looked up, finding his face too close for comfort, and suddenly her heart was thudding. Their mouths met in an explosive move-

ment. It was not one-sided—Kate had to recognise
that. Her mouth clung to his and the hands holding her
slid round her body and tightened. An overpowering
heat filled her veins. Her body was plastic, yielding,
her hands holding his broad shoulders as if for support.

It was Eliot who ended it. He pushed her away,
breathing thickly. The elevator doors had opened and
a woman in a trim lavender dress and silvery hair was
looking at them with distaste. They stumbled out of
the elevator and she walked into it, turning her elegant
head away.

As she vanished behind the closing doors Eliot burst
into a roar of laughter. 'What a face!'

Kate could not help laughing back. 'We shocked
her.'

'I expect she'll complain to the management,' Eliot
suggested, grinning at her.

'Lucky we're leaving tomorrow. I don't fancy getting
evicted from the hotel,' said Kate, still smiling.

'No,' he agreed. 'It would look bad in the papers.'

They had reached her door and she got out her key,
still flushed, suddenly aware that he was not moving,
standing beside her watching her with those cool,
aware grey eyes.

'Goodnight,' she mumbled.

He laughed shortly. 'Goodnight, Kate.'

He turned on his heel and she opened her door and
slid quickly into the room, glad to close the door
safely on the temptation she knew he had been offering
her.

She lay in bed and faced the fact that she had been
tempted. She hadn't even had time to consider it while
she was in Eliot's arms in the elevator. One minute she

had been feeling irritated and fed up, the next she had been overtaken by a rising flood of feeling which carried her away with it. Ever since Toby's death she had been sealed off, entombed like a fly in amber, safe from the sexual drive which she had learnt to dread. A burnt child fears the fire. Kate had not had to teach herself to shun men—her experience with Toby had done that for her and she had imagined she was immune for life. She had learnt that sexual pleasure brought with it danger, pain, humiliation. Her subconscious dread of it had made her aggressive whenever she was placed in a sexual situation. She attacked before she could be attacked.

What was happening to her now was something she had not expected. Urges she was terrified by had begun to dominate her. Her body had apparently developed a life of its own, rejecting the commands of her mind. Her subconscious shrieked: Danger! whenever Eliot took a step too close, but her treacherous senses clamoured for the pleasure he was capable of giving her. The automatic reflex which made the child's hand leap back from the fire was not working in her case now; something had jammed the system.

She fell asleep with difficulty and stirred crossly when the phone went. It was her early morning call. Struggling out of bed, her head throbbing, she made her way into the bathroom. She was dressed when her tray arrived. The young floor waiter gave her a little wink and a grin. She drank the coffee, leaving her croissants untouched. She had no appetite this morning.

Bordeaux was under the same vivid blue sky which was covering most of France and England. The weather had been unbroken for weeks, a halcyon summer which seemed to go on and on without change. Steve Martin's cheerful energy irritated her today. He ought to be flagging after his nights of amusement, but he wasn't. If anything he was very cheerful.

Eliot and Kate drove around looking at factories and talking to businessmen. Steve got a few pictures of a modern farm and then some of a small, archaic place run by three taciturn brothers who only said as little as possible. The question of the 'green pound' was more than a political issue in France. The feelings of the French farmer ran high when it came to the agricultural policy of the common market. France was still a far more rural economy than was the case in England and it made a strong talking-point in the interviews Eliot was having.

They had dinner with an affluent gentleman who had met Eliot in America. Kate was treated with enormous courtesy, but it was Eliot and the other man who did all the talking, exchanging views on the current American political situation, gossip about mutual friends over there, wry comment on the present French–American relationship. The Frenchman had a beautifully unreal accent, Americanised French, theatrical and charming. He seemed unaware of it, talking briskly, using his well-kept dark-haired hands all the time in the quick continental gestures which betrayed his origin.

'Off the record, Eliot,' he kept saying with a dart of his cynical black eyes before he made some outrageous comment, and Eliot grinned.

'If I quoted you there could be an international incident, Michel.'

From time to time they would one of them remember Kate's presence and turn to her to ask if her veal was tender, her wine drinkable, her coffee as she liked it. Kate smiled and nodded and would have liked to kick them. They didn't even know they were doing it, treating her as if she were a child or an animal, with courteous contempt; charming, indulgent and infuriating.

When they parted from the Frenchman he kissed Kate's hand with a bow, giving her an admiring little glance, murmuring a few words of automatic gallantry.

Eliot eyed her shrewdly as they returned to their hotel in a taxi. 'Do I detect some smouldering going on under that cool little face?'

'No,' Kate said ironically. 'I just love being ignored for a whole evening.'

'Ignored?' He arched a brow derisively. 'Michel couldn't have been more impressed. Compliments flowed faster than the wine.'

She shrugged an irritated shoulder. 'Oh, he made a few magic passes in my direction, but that wasn't what I meant. You talked to him all evening. I might as well not have been there.'

'That was the point of the evening, honey,' Eliot pointed out. 'I was getting an interview.'

'Off the record,' she retorted.

He grinned. 'Oh, those were just personal views. He said a lot I could use. I know the dividing line and Michel trusts me.' His finger touched her bare arm, slid along the smooth curve of it sensuously. 'Stop scowling.' There was huskiness in his voice.

They arrived at the hotel and went up to their rooms. Kate inserted her key into the door of her own room and turned, her face flushed and wary. 'Goodnight.'

Eliot's eyes held a brilliant amusement. He moved closer and Kate could not stop what happened to her. She lifted her face and met the searching probe of his kiss without reserve, giving way to the need which had been nagging away at her all evening. She had sat at that table and listened to the two men with a cool face, but under her calm she had been obsessed with the hunger throbbing away deep inside her body. She had watched every turn of Eliot's smooth head, every movement of his hands, the lithe grace with which he reached across the table or leaned back, laughing. Her mind had shut off at the conscious level. She had been a camera carefully recording the small details of Eliot's voice, smile, long-limbed body.

She had resented his concentration on his friend. She had been jealous, angry, so deeply absorbed in him that she was furious because he showed no sign of returning that absorption.

Now she began to tremble violently, her arms round his neck, the demanding potency of his kiss deepening as he felt her responding to it. Her head fell back with a faint moan as he slid his lips hotly down her neck. She felt urgency flaring in him. His hands stroked down her body and slid up again to find the small, high breasts, and her heart ran out of control, racing wildly.

Eliot muttered into her throat, 'I want you, Kate.' She did not have to tell him that he had aroused her; the fingers softly caressing her had discovered that. Under her thin silk dress his caress had hardened the thrust of her breasts, made her sexual excitement very obvious.

Through the hazy heat of her own desire she heard a cold still voice. She would have liked to shut it out, ignore it, but it had the force of too much pain behind it. She dragged herself back, holding Eliot at a distance, her hands on his shoulders. 'I can't,' she whispered hoarsely. 'Please don't!'

She could sense the surge of passion in him even without looking at him, but when she did look up his eyes were hectic, flashing with desire, burning on her in fixed demand.

'I won't hurt you,' he said unsteadily. 'Believe me, Kate. Trust me. The last thing I want to do is frighten or hurt you. Let me near you, darling. Love me.' His hand reached up and stroked her hot cheek tenderly. 'Love me, darling. Don't turn me off again.'

The sexual urgency in his eyes made her shudder, fear engulfing all the yielding sweetness of her own passion. He might promise he wouldn't hurt her, but he had not kept his word last time—he had used force, his body cruel, his face hostile.

'No,' Kate said bitterly, and leapt back before he guessed what she meant to do. The door slammed between them and she stood there, shaking, panic-stricken, because as she slammed the door she had seen biting fury in his grey eyes.

CHAPTER NINE

THEIR final day in France was a frenzied dash from place to place with the prospect of getting a plane back to England at eight o'clock that evening always hanging in front of them like a guillotine. Steve Martin had relapsed into his previous gloom—Kate gathered from the few laconic comments he dropped that he had not enjoyed his evening in Bordeaux and, in consequence, was irritable. Physical exhaustion had caught up with him. He yawned a good deal and was snappy. His ill temper covered Eliot's, making it easier for Kate to ignore the clipped tone of Eliot's voice, the barbed little remarks, the icy stare of his eyes.

He was furious with her—he made that obvious. As they went from appointment to appointment he barely spoke and when he did she winced at the sting of his voice.

She realised that she had given his ego something of a blow. Last night he had known very well that he was getting response from her and when she shut the door on him his face had been violent.

She was sufficiently regretful to try placating him, keeping her own temper down, speaking to him evenly, patiently.

It didn't seem to work. The more she tried to soothe him down the more his face tightened, his eyes bit into her. She wasn't too surprised. She might have rejected him, but it had been a struggle and she knew how it must have felt—she had been torn by contrary impulses, lying awake for hours afterwards aching with a fevered desire she could not fight.

They flew back to England on time, parted from Steve and drove back into London together. Eliot dropped her at her apartment, his curt nod of farewell accompanied with the words, 'See you.'

She did not see him for two days and when he came into the office on the Friday morning she was on the telephone, laughing at something Dee was telling her about Kevin. She glanced across the room and met the inimical grey eyes, hiding her flinch as well as she could.

'Right, Dee,' she said, her voice warmer than it would have been because Eliot was listening. 'Dinner tomorrow, then.' She put the phone down and Mirry gave her a funny sideways look before winding the new sheet of paper into her typewriter.

'I've done my stuff,' Kate said to Eliot politely, picking up the folder of work and offering it to him.

He looked at it as though it might bite. 'So I should hope. Did the other pages come in?'

'Yes.' She had those too, lying on her desk, and picked them up. He took them and stalked back to his desk without a word. What a delightful man you are, Kate thought, staring at him. Was he going to go around in this nasty mood for ever? He had made a few determined passes and because she had turned him down it apparently made her public enemy number one. The nerve of it made her hair prickle on the back of her head. All he imagined he had to do was whistle to have her fall swooning into his manly arms.

During her two days away from him she had had time to think. The mounting tension of her attraction towards him had died away, but it had left her doubly on her guard, aware now of his potential as a risk.

He was a very self-aware operator. Had his campaign against her all been planned? Had he hoped to sweep her off her feet while they were in France and away from the confines of the office? It had almost worked. A few kisses, a few whispered phrases and she had been half committed. Only the last remnant of common sense had stopped her from making an almighty fool of herself.

She bent over her work, her black head hiding her expression. Well, she wouldn't make that mistake again. She wouldn't let Mr Eliot Holman get within fifty feet of her without screaming.

The weather broke that evening in a sudden thunderstorm which had been threatening all day in sultry, humid heat and grey skies. Rain poured from the sky and the London streets which had so recently been baking with heat were dancing and thudding with great cloudbursts.

Kate got soaked going home. She had come out, in common with most Londoners, expecting the unvarying blue skies of recent weeks and she was wet from head to foot when she let herself into her apartment, the hair clinging to her head in damp strands.

She got into a loose kaftan and made herself a meal, listening to the news on the radio while she ate. Standing at the window, she looked at the lowering skies. Summer would be over soon.

Next day she did her shopping and tidied the apartment, had lunch at a local restaurant because she did not feel like cooking and then went back to her apartment to get ready for the evening she was spending with Judy and Dee.

In honour of the occasion she took some trouble

with her looks; picking out her coral dress to wear, brushing her black hair until it shone and lingering over her make-up.

Dee had told her that this was to be the first dinner party he and Judy had given since they remarried. It was a celebration. 'Just a few close friends,' he had told her. 'And we want you particularly. We both feel we owe you a debt of gratitude. If you hadn't told me what crazy ideas Judy was harbouring I'd never have found out and I might well have done Eliot an injury.'

Kate had laughed. 'All it took was a little common sense.'

'Judy might have had some in the first place,' Dee had grunted.

'Judy was too emotionally involved.' Kate had paused. 'She was afraid you might have been tempted by a ravishing little dolly, and some men are, Dee. You know that.'

'I'm not some men,' he had come back. 'Judy ought to have known that.'

'Love isn't always logical,' Kate had suggested.

He laughed wryly. 'No, so I found out. My God, the fantasies I cherished about what I'd do to Eliot! And when I told Judy she just roared with laughter.'

'There you are, then,' Kate had smiled.

'As you say, there we are, and thank you very much,' Dee had told her warmly. 'We'll never forget it, either of us.'

Kate was very happy for them. It was wonderful to see the change in them both. Judy's sad face had disturbed her for a long time. Kate's instincts had been to see it all from Judy's point of view and she could imagine the pain Judy had suffered. It disturbed

Kate that part of that pain had been through her. She should never have gone to see *Scheherazade* with Dee, although it had all been perfectly innocent. Looking back, she could have kicked herself. But at the time she had been so sure that Judy was involved with Eliot, and now she recognised her own secret jealousy over that. She hadn't even admitted the possibility at the time, but she had to admit it now.

Dee had said on the phone that he would send a taxi for her. Kate had protested lightly and he had told her to do as she was told. 'I'll arrange it,' he had said in a firm tone which left no room for argument.

When the ring came at the door bell Kate took a final glance at herself, was satisfied with what she saw and went to answer it.

She stared in shock at Eliot. 'Ready?' he asked curtly.

She understood in a second. 'You're my taxi?'

'For tonight,' he said with a faint cold smile.

Dee might have told her. Had that been deliberate? She eyed Eliot and got nothing but cool regard in return. He was wearing a dark lounge suit, striped shirt and dark silk tie and he looked both elegant and withdrawn, the fair gleam of his head smoothly brushed down, the hard features wary.

She followed him down to his car and watched him handling it as they drove. 'Still raining, I see,' she observed conversationally.

'Keen eyesight, obviously,' Eliot said nastily.

So that was to be his attitude, she thought, her lips straightening. Right. She lapsed back into silence, staring out of the window.

There were four other guests—all of them from the

paper, all of them well known to both Kate and Eliot. It was a simple matter for her to talk to one or the other of them without so much as looking at Eliot, and a simple matter for him to do the same. As they sipped their drinks before dinner they stood around talking in a little group, occasionally moving away to look at a picture on the wall or throw an eye over the bookcases.

Judy drew Kate out to the kitchen, talking to her. 'Have a good time in France?'

Kate felt the interested gleam in her eye, but her face was guarded. 'Busy. We had a tight schedule.'

'Dee says the ads. people are pleased with the way it's going.'

'Lots of foreign banks advertising with us,' Kate agreed.

'Why is it always banks?'

'They're the ones with the money,' Kate said.

Judy laughed. 'How horribly true!'

Kate was helping her with the final preparations. They were eating a carefully worked-out meal which was prepared in advance and served with the minimum of fuss by Judy at the last minute—melon, a dish of scampi and rice which was simmering in the oven now, followed by a huge chocolate cream or green figs.

'Kevin in bed?' Kate asked her.

'Supposed to be,' Judy agreed. 'But actually he has the portable television in there and he'll stay awake as long as he can manage, watching a Western that's on tonight.'

'Everything O.K. between you and Dee?' Kate asked her, and Judy grinned at her.

'Except that I feel a fool, yes. My God, he yelled at

me when he realised! I've rarely seen Dee so angry.'

'I hate to say I told you so,' Kate laughed.

'Then don't,' Judy laughed back. 'But you were so right. I behaved like an idiot.' She looked down at the bowl of powdered ginger she was holding. 'Talking about idiots, why are you and Eliot studiously ignoring each other?'

Kate felt herself going hot. 'Oh, it's a long story.'

Judy looked up. 'And mind my own business?'

Kate smiled at her dry tone. 'Would you mind if I said yes?'

'Consider the subject closed,' Judy said as she walked away. 'It's just that I like both of you and I wouldn't have eyes in my head if I hadn't noticed long ago that Eliot fancies you.'

Judy didn't wait for a reply, which was just as well, since Kate didn't have one to give. It was no news to her that Eliot Holman fancied her. He had made that very clear. Kate would be less than human if she didn't enjoy the knowledge, but it made no difference. She had admitted to herself now that she more than fancied him, that her body had known before her heart that she was falling badly for him, but despite all that Kate refused to abandon herself again to the rough seas of passion. On that sea she was no sailor. She had come to grief on her only other voyage and she had no mind to be shipwrecked and marooned again.

She carried the melon into the dining-room and Judy looked up from the mats she was placing. 'You don't know how lucky you are,' Kate told her. 'Even having had that bad time over Dee, you've still got yourself a fantastic man and he loves you. What if it had all been true, Judy? What if Dee had been cheating

you all through your marriage? You wouldn't be so
ready to risk it again, believe me.'

Judy shifted a glass and stared at it. 'Dee told me
about your husband.'

'Excusing himself?' Kate asked drily.

Judy laughed briefly. 'Something of the sort. It
was tough luck, but all men aren't cut on the same
lines.'

'Maybe.' Kate turned to go.

'Eliot certainly isn't,' Judy said in restless defence.
'I've known him for years. He's as straight as a die
and a good friend. I'd trust him with my life.'

'Lucky you don't have to,' Kate said with a bite.
'Have you ever seen him when he's really in a temper?'
She thought of the savage icy eyes she had seen as she
closed the door on him that night in France. 'You only
see him in contexts he chooses. People are deceptive,
Judy.'

Judy was flushed and aggressive now, springing to
his defence with loyal warmth. 'People can't hide their
natures for as long as I've known Eliot. He's kind,
helpful and sympathetic.'

But then, Kate thought drily, he doesn't want to
sleep with you and you haven't turned him down when
he thought he was getting somewhere. But she did not
say that aloud. Instead she said quietly, 'Let's agree
to differ, shall we?'

The complications which sexual relations could
cause were endless and unpredictable. Eliot might be
a kind, even-tempered friend, but Kate had already discovered that he had another side to his nature. Frustrated, he became violent, and it was that violence
which Kate feared above everything else. There was

no reason in love. It was a drug which had unknown side effects and which acted differently on each individual. One couldn't guess what it would do. One experimented at one's own risk, and Kate was taking no more risks.

The dinner table was lively and amusing. Somehow the silence between Kate and Eliot managed to pass unnoticed more or less. Now and then her eyes met his across the table and each time they both looked away.

As the evening wore on Kate found herself becoming tense at the realisation that she would have to drive home with him afterwards. The rain had slackened now and the night was fine and mild, slightly cool, the gardens freshly scented from the long-deferred downpour which had put new life back into baked earth and dried-up lawns.

Dee saw them off at the door, expansive, a cigar in his hand, calling out warnings about driving on wet roads.

Kate sat beside Eliot as they moved off in the car and searched her mind vainly for some polite remark which wouldn't expose her to one of his biting retorts.

He didn't say a word, his head averted from her. The street lamps flashed past, giving a brief illumination to the interior of the car. 'Music?' Eliot asked drily at last, giving her a brief look.

She leaned forward and fiddled with the dials on his radio, finding some mournful cello music which had a dying fall.

'Oh, perfect,' Eliot said ironically. 'Just what I'm in the mood for.'

'Shall I find something else?' She flashed across the

wavebands and a gabble of foreign voices and hectic pop music poured out at them.

'Let's have the cello,' Eliot muttered.

They heard the rest of the concerto. By the time it had ended and the smooth BBC voice had given the artist's name and burbled on about the composer, they had got to Kate's apartment. Eliot switched off the engine and the radio died.

He turned and gave her a cool nod. 'I won't be so optimistic as to expect a cup of coffee.'

She prickled with annoyance at his tone. 'Why not? Come up if you want some coffee.'

Even as she said it she wanted to take it back because she was asking for trouble. She had the feeling it had been a deliberate barb delivered in the precise hope of making her mad enough to invite him in, but it was too late to realise that now. He was already out of the car and she unhappily followed him into the apartment.

He wandered around while she made the coffee, inspecting the place like an estate agent doubtful of making a sale, insolently surveying her books and records, lifting his brows at the furniture and skimming his eyes over the photographs of her family.

When she sat down and poured out the coffee he wandered back to her and took a seat beside her. 'Your brother?' he asked, nodding at the enormous studio portrait of Oliver which her mother had bestowed on her the previous Christmas.

'I'm not too flattered that you should recognise any resemblance,' she said lightly.

Eliot stirred his coffee. 'All the same, there is one. Are there only two of you?'

'Just two,' she agreed. 'Oliver would be enough for my mother on his own.'

He shot her a quick look. 'Oh?'

'She dotes on him.'

Eliot's brows lifted again. 'Do I detect a note of jealousy?'

'It was just a statement of fact.'

He smiled coldly. 'Was he the voice on the phone?'

She stared in blank bewilderment.

'When I rang you,' he reminded.

She began to laugh. 'Oh, yes, that was Oliver. Sorry —his idea of a joke.'

'Odd sense of humour. A remark like that could cause trouble.'

'That wouldn't bother him. Trouble is what he lives for.'

'A family trait,' he said sardonically.

Kate flushed. Glancing at his cup she asked quickly, 'More coffee, or have you had enough?'

He didn't say anything, just held out his cup. She poured him some more coffee and glanced at the clock, and Eliot caught the movement of her eyes. 'Getting late, is it?' he asked in the same sardonic tone. 'Does it matter? It's Sunday tomorrow.'

'I'm spending it with my family, though,' Kate said quickly. 'And I do want to get to bed.'

'So do I,' Eliot said softly, staring at her, and her face filled with heat. On an involuntary reflex she began to get up and he lifted a lazy arm to grab her wrist. 'Don't,' Kate muttered, tugging at her trapped hand.

He jerked on it and she lost her balance. Eliot pulled her sideways so that she fell across his lap, her eyes flashing in alarm to his face.

His half-smile died as he saw the expression she wore. 'Don't shiver when I touch you,' he broke out. 'What have I done to make you look at me like that?'

'You didn't see your face when I shut you out of my room,' Kate flung back huskily.

'Are you surprised?' His skin took on a dark red heat, his eyes fixed in dangerous anger. 'If my self-control hadn't been good, I'd have smashed that door down. As it was, it took half a bottle of whisky to get me to sleep.'

'You're lucky. I didn't have any whisky.'

As she said it her heart missed a beat from sheer horror. She could have bitten her tongue out. Eliot stared down at her, the grey eyes narrowing, the hand-some face intent. Kate looked away from the sharp probe of those eyes, knowing what she had given away and furious with herself.

'So,' he said slowly, his voice husky. 'You weren't just teasing me?'

Kate couldn't answer and after a moment he lifted her chin and made her look at him. 'Did you want me, Kate?' he asked softly.

Her eyes restlessly slid away from him and she folded her mouth into a straight, defensive line.

His hand moved down her back, making her spine tingle. 'I thought you were having a game with me, teasing, leading me on,' he said very quietly. 'I could see how you would get some fun out of that. Your husband had you on a rack, so you enjoy doing the same to others.'

'No,' she protested in a low, husky voice.

'No?' His finger touched her lips and she quivered. 'Do you have any idea how I felt? You might have let me down lightly. One minute I was getting some-where, the next I was facing a door.'

'It's no good,' Kate mumbled. 'I can't do it, Eliot.'

'You still haven't answered my question,' he re-turned in that soft voice. 'Did you want me? Do you?'

She couldn't look at him, her eyes on the dark line of his silk tie. 'It makes no difference.'

'It does to me.' He sounded half angry, half amused.

She shrugged, staring at his tie.

'Very well,' Eliot said silkily. 'If we can't get the answer one way, we'll get it another.'

'No!' she burst out in panic as she realised what he meant, but he was tilting her like a child, her slender body cradled in his arms, and while she was still pro-testing he took her lips in a ruthless, demanding kiss that silenced her and awoke her body into clamouring life.

The yielding weakness that swept over her horrified her. She felt her control over herself snapping. The hunger she had tried to suppress broke free of the bonds she had placed on it, and she struggled like someone drowning under the impact of what was go-ing on inside her own body.

Eliot's hard mouth softened as he felt the response she was unwillingly betraying. The kiss coaxed, per-suaded, seduced; and his hands slid silkily down her body and sent excited signals flashing to her brain.

He manipulated her zipper, his hands slipping in-side her dress to stroke the warm, smooth skin, and Kate mumbled, 'No,' the word muffled by the drug-ging seduction of his mouth against her own.

She put up her hands to push his head away, but Eliot tilted her further, making her helpless, his lips deepening their kiss. Kate's hands took their own path, stroking the smooth thick hair, fondling his neck and following the strong line of his shoulders.

Eliot lifted his head and the grey eyes pierced hers, reading the desire she couldn't hide.

'Say it,' he muttered. 'Tell me, Kate.'

She stared at him, her eyes frightened, bright blue. 'I can't.'

'I'm not asking for possession of you body and soul,' he said in tense deliberation. 'I don't want a human sacrifice. What are you afraid of? I won't force anything out of you. I just want to make love to you, and I think you want it, too.'

'No commitment?' she stammered.

'No commitment,' Eliot whispered, watching her. 'Just love, Kate. Love me and don't count costs.'

As his mouth lowered she met it urgently, her hands running over his back and shoulders in an increasing restlessness, the sensual need she had been fighting now in complete command of her. Eliot dropped his jacket to the floor, tugged off his tie. Kate watched him as he undid his shirt, her mouth dry, staring at the smooth gleam of his skin, the wide muscled shoulders and lean chest. He glanced down at her and their eyes held silently.

Slowly he bent and she surrendered, coming to fierce life as the long fingers caressed her body, beginning to give muffled little moans of pleasure at what he was doing. The power of the sexual drive she had for years suppressed and stifled rose like a tidal wave, drowning all thought. She existed in a mindless excitement, trembling, running her hands over him and hearing the way his heart thudded as she did so.

Breathless, she felt his mouth halt, his head lift again. He was pale, his face taut. 'Tell me, Kate,' he asked in a slurred voice. 'Tell me you love me.'

The stab of fear which shot through her was so savage and so sudden that she gasped and whitened.

He stared, a frown coming into his face. 'What's wrong?'

She couldn't speak, only stare, shuddering.

'Don't you?' he demanded, and his voice had become harsh now. He watched her intently, his eyes hardening.

Kate struggled to get up and he held her down. 'Is that it?' he asked sharply. 'Tell me!'

Kate saw the great black hole opening in front of her. She stared into it and knew she did not have the courage to dare that darkness, that terrifying plunge into the unknown.

Slowly she shook her head, her eyes falling away from him. Eliot held her chin in one hand, watching her face. 'Did you love him?'

The question baffled her. She looked up guardedly to find his face expressionless, impossible to decipher. Realising what he had meant, she said wryly, 'My husband? Oh, yes. I was eighteen and Toby was a fabulous man. I thought the sun shone out of him. At eighteen you have an almost boundless capacity for love, and you're easily taken in by looks.'

'What did he look like?' Eliot was talking in a calm, slow voice which held no particular emotion, but his lids were shielding his eyes and her senses picked up something else beneath that deceptive surface.

She shrugged. 'Tall, fair . . .'

'Ah,' Eliot muttered, and she stopped. His lids rose and the grey eyes were steely. 'Do I remind you of him?'

'Not in looks.' She said that quickly and he picked up the faint unspoken thought.

'In some ways, though?'

She hesitated, biting her lip. 'You can get violent.' She saw his mouth tighten and said quickly, 'Well, it's true! You can be alarming when you're angry. You're angry now. Do you think I can't feel it? I can feel the vibrations even when you aren't saying or doing anything.'

'And you feel threatened?'

She nodded, a faint shiver running down her spine. That was exactly what she felt—threatened, in danger, faced with the fear of the unknown and unpredictable.

He laughed curtly. 'So you should. My God, Kate, I've no wish to frighten you, but I'm a man, not a boy, and for a long time I've been aching to make love to you. If I'm angry, it's because I'm frustrated, and frustration has its own sort of anger. Maybe you know that. Maybe you're doing just what I thought you were doing when we were in France—you're having fun, teasing me.'

She gave him a bitter little smile. 'Do you really think I'd have the nerve? I'd be too scared of what might happen.'

'Who'd have thought it?' Eliot's grey eyes mocked her contemptuously. 'And I imagined you had enough nerve for anything! So under all the tough talking, you're just a trembling little coward. The way you run the department anyone would think you were lion-hearted! And it's all a front, is it, Kate?'

Furiously she stared back at him. 'Shut up!'

'I remember you telling me I couldn't frighten you,' he mocked. 'All lies, was it? Covering up? You little fraud!'

Her temper shot through the top of her head. 'No man is ever going to slap me around again and then make me go to bed with him. I'd rather jump off the top of St Paul's!'

'It isn't me you're scared of, Kate,' Eliot said very softly, his eyes bright. 'It's yourself. You don't think you can take me, do you? In your eyes it's a war and you don't think you've got the weapons to match mine. And you're right, of course, if you're trying to fight as if you were a man, too. But you're not a man, Kate. You're a woman and you've got weapons that outgun me every time. You just don't use them.'

He put her down on to the sofa and rose, doing up his shirt. Kate stared at him, frowning. He bent and picked up his tie, slung it round his neck and hooked his jacket over his shoulder before looking down at her with a sardonic smile.

'Think about it, Kate. Sure, you may lose the occasional battle, but my God! you can win the war.'

He went, and she listened to the quiet closing of the front door, not moving, her face blank.

CHAPTER TEN

SHE was working at her desk when Eliot sauntered into the office the following Monday. Kate felt the quick look he gave her and glanced up, but he was already smiling at Mirry, his head turned away from her. 'Good weekend?' he asked, and Mirry answered, smiling back. Kate looked back at her desk, her teeth gritting. Every time she saw Mirry gazing at him with enormous adoring eyes it made her want to scream.

Roger popped his head round the door halfway through the morning and said, 'Eliot, can I have a word?'

The smooth fair head lifted. 'Mmm?' Eliot had an abstracted note in his voice as he focused on Roger.

'In my office,' Roger said. 'I've got someone special to see you.'

Eliot surveyed him cynically. 'After more space, Roger?'

Roger grinned. 'You don't want to meet Marise Filon?'

Mirry exclaimed, open-mouthed, and Eliot got up. 'Really? What's she doing in your office? What are you up to, Roger?'

They went out and Kate stared after them, the back of her neck prickling. Mirry looked across the room at her excitedly. 'Have you read her book? I couldn't put it down.'

'I haven't read it,' Kate told her briskly. 'Are those letters finished?'

'They're making a film of it,' Mirry went on, dis-

regarding the question. 'They say it's autobiographical
—the book, I mean. There's a picture of her on the
back cover. She looks just like the heroine.'

Kate sighed wearily. 'The letters, Mirry.'

Mirry gave her one of her sulky looks and went back
to her work. Kate looked down at the copy she was
working on and didn't see a word of it. She hadn't
read the book, but she had seen a picture of Marise
Filon. She knew what had put that hectic look into
Roger's eyes and what had sent Eliot hurrying off to
meet her.

Eliot did not come back before lunch. Mirry dumped
the letters on Kate's desk and vanished. Kate signed
them, put them back on Mirry's desk and went down to
the canteen. Judy waved to her from a table and
she joined her.

Judy grinned at her as she sat down. 'I hear you've
had Marise Filon in the Features Department today.'

'My God, the grapevine works well.' Kate looked at
her cheese salad with distaste. 'I'm sure this cheese is
several days old. It looks like grated cement.'

'Is she as ravishing as her pictures?' Judy pursued.

'I couldn't say. I didn't see her.' Kate sipped some
of her black coffee. 'Eliot went off to meet her, though.'

'I believe it, I believe it,' Judy carolled, grinning.
'Have you read it?'

'No. Have you?'

'From cover to cover. If it's true that it's autobiographical, she's packed a lot into her life.'

'She certainly raised some dust in the department,'
said Kate, poking her cheese with a reluctant fork.
'Roger was as excited as I've ever seen him, and Mirry
was dying to ask for her autograph.'

'And Eliot?' Judy asked drily.

Kate kept her eyes on her plate. 'I didn't notice him dragging his feet when Roger fetched him to meet her.'

'I see,' Judy drawled.

Kate lifted her head, eyes flashing. 'What's that supposed to mean?'

'I've noticed it before,' Judy said in a considering voice.

'What?' Kate pushed her uneaten meal away.

Judy met her aggressive stare directly. 'You're interested in him, aren't you?'

Kate got up. 'I'm interested in crocodiles, but I don't get into a tank with them.'

As she walked away, Judy was still laughing, but Kate wasn't even smiling. She took a longer lunch hour than usual, browsing through a bookshop in an alley off Fleet Street, but when she got back to the office Mirry was there alone. There was no sign of Eliot. The day moved on and he still did not come back. Kate irritably coped with the work alone and when Mirry went she glanced at the clock and told herself that she was going dead on six-thirty. It was not her night turn. If he chose to walk off without making arrangements to swap, that was his affair, not hers.

Of course, she didn't. Someone had to see the galleys when they came up and although it would serve Eliot right if she just walked off and let him explain to Dee why the department had been empty, she didn't actually do it in the end. She worked at her desk listening to the low hum of the traffic as London emptied for the night, hearing the rumbling of the machines down in the bowels of the building, the strange empty echo of the corridors now that the day staff had gone.

At eight o'clock the door opened and Eliot strolled in, glancing at her with lifted eyebrows. 'Not gone yet?'

Kate's temper was close to boiling point. 'Does it look like it?'

'Don't snap at me,' he said with a cold flick of the eyes.

'Next time you want to drop everything and rush off with a possible conquest you might take five minutes to make arrangements to have your work done,' Kate said furiously. 'I've had to work non-stop all afternoon and, in case you'd forgotten, it was my night off.'

'I hadn't forgotten,' he told her crisply. 'I'm back, aren't I?'

'A bit late.' She got up and went to pick up her coat. Eliot stepped into her path and gave her a long, hard look.

'Why are you shrieking at me? Or can I guess?'

'I don't like being left to carry the department without warning,' Kate said.

'You wouldn't be jealous?' he asked drily.

'No,' Kate burst out violently, 'I wouldn't.'

'No, nothing so human,' Eliot jeered. 'You wouldn't know how, would you?'

Kate felt a stab of rage so painful that her face went white with it. She looked at him briefly and stepped past him. Without a word she grabbed her coat and went.

In the lift going down she thought of the hours he had been absent and savagely guessed at what he had been doing. Not human, she thought, clamping her teeth together. Oh, aren't I? I'll show him!

When she got down to the main door it was pelting with rain, the drops bouncing off the pavements and splashing the marble steps. She paused, looking at the dark street with reluctance, and the night porter said helpfully: 'Raining, I'm afraid, Miss Marchant.'

Kate gave him a wide, insincere smile. 'Cats and dogs. This is where I wish I had a magic carpet.'

'What you want's a taxi,' said someone behind her, and she looked round at Steve Martin. He was festooned with cameras and looking as gloomy as ever, eyeing the rainy night with something of her own annoyance.

'Shall I ring for one, miss?' the porter asked, hovering.

Kate hesitated. 'Yes, please,' she said at last.

He moved away and Steve asked: 'Where are you going? Not passing Swiss Cottage, I suppose?'

She glanced at him. 'Close enough. I live at St John's Wood.'

'We could share the taxi,' he suggested. 'I don't want to get my cameras wet.'

Kate laughed. 'You and your cameras! Why not?'

'Taxi on its way, miss,' the porter told them, beaming.

As she had discovered in France, Steve Martin had a laconic style of conversation, limiting himself to the very tersest comments. As they drove through the rainy streets he muttered a few words about the weather and asked: 'French stuff come out all right?'

'As far as I know.'

'I got a honey of a picture from the Eiffel Tower, but Eliot wouldn't use it.' He glared out of the window at the fuzzy yellow circles on the rain-wet pavements where the light spilled from street lamps. 'Good shot, that was.'

'What a pity,' Kate said absently, thinking of other things.

'Yeah. He's using the pics of those two old birds instead.'

'The politicians?'

Steve nodded. 'Dead boring. No imagination, that's Eliot's trouble.'

Kate looked at him, her eyes flashing. 'That's true.'

'Got some of you,' Steve said with a sudden grin, his eyes very bright. 'Want to see them?'

They were turning into the main road from which Kate's road was reached and her eyes were on the driver. 'I'd love to,' she said vaguely.

'Right.' Steve leaned forward and tapped the window. 'Skip the St John's Wood address and go on to Swiss Cottage,' he said.

Kate sat up, startled. 'I . . .'

'You'll like them,' Steve said in self-congratulation. 'I got about a dozen of you and Eliot—one or two are really honeys. You take well. Some people look really horrible, d'you know that? You can never tell, either. It's always a surprise the way a shot comes out.'

The taxi had already sped past Kate's road. She sat back, fuming. She hadn't been listening to a word Steve had said and now she was stuck with an hour longer in his company. He was talking again and she nodded politely, only half listening. On a night like this the last thing she wanted to do was look at pictures.

Steve lived in a very large double-fronted house split into a number of tiny apartments. He had one on the ground floor and as he let them into it Kate heard the clash of jazz from a room opposite. 'Clarinettist,' Steve mumbled, seeing her head turn.

'Has he got a whole jazz group in there?' The decibels were making the walls rock.

'Just a record,' said Steve, laughing in his abrupt way. He switched on the light and gestured. 'Make yourself at home. Sorry about the mess.'

So am I, Kate thought, staring round the crowded uncomfortable little room. The walls were hung with prints of photographs pinned there with drawing-pins and magazines and newspapers were scattered around like confetti.

Steve vanished behind a curtain and came back to ask: 'Coffee?'

'Thank you, but I can't stop long,' Kate said, beginning suddenly to feel a little nervous.

Steve winked. 'Don't worry. You can ring for a taxi home from here.' He glanced round the room. 'Knock something off a chair and sit down. You look as if you're going to go the minute I take my eye off you. I'll make some sandwiches. How about toasted bacon?'

Kate was hungry suddenly, realising that she had not eaten the cheese salad she had stupidly bought at lunch. 'That sounds great,' she agreed. 'Thanks.'

'My pleasure.' He vanished behind the curtain and Kate went over to peer round it at him. The tiny kitchenette was amazingly clean and neat and as he heard her movements he turned to grin. 'Well, come in, then. It won't bite you.'

'Can I help?'

'Many hands, etc,' he said, opening a small fridge. 'You cut the bread, I'll get the bacon.'

They worked in almost silence. Steve whistled as he

moved around. Looking at her, he asked: 'You're Eliot's bird, aren't you?'

Kate almost retorted a firm no and then paused. She wasn't sure about Steve Martin. 'We're good friends,' she said drily.

Steve laughed. 'I spotted that. Fancies you, doesn't he? Didn't take his eyes off you while we were in Paris. You can see that in my shots—every one of them.'

They ate their snack and drank their coffee in the kitchenette. It was only just big enough to sit down in, but Kate felt it was preferable to the slum conditions in the other room.

'I'll get the prints,' said Steve, rising. 'Leave the washing up.'

She cleared some space on a chair and sat down. Steve came in with a big sheaf of glossy prints and handed them to her one by one with comments. Kate looked at herself and Eliot and knew that anyone who saw those pictures would find it hard to miss the attraction prickling between them. Steve had taken them without their knowledge and he had caught turns of the head, expressions of the eye, that were all too revealing.

'How about these, then?' Steve demanded, handing her some more pictures with a broad grin.

She glanced at them and raised her eyebrows. 'Eliot won't be using any of these,' she told him sardonically.

'You can say that again. They're for my private collection,' Steve laughed.

They were all of pretty girls, some taken in the street, some in what seemed to be a nightclub. Kate had seen far more revealing pictures in magazines, but Steve's obsession with camera angles gave these pictures an unusual twist. Sometimes he had concentrated on legs, sometimes on faces, and they were extremely well framed shots, clever angles, often funny ones.

Kate glanced at her watch. 'Oh, heavens, it's half past ten!' She had never expected to stay in the apartment so late, but Steve's pet obsession was hard to avoid. He only ever talked with any excitement about either photography or women and his face, which was normally gloomy, could light up with interest on either subject.

'I'll get you a taxi,' he promised, moving to the phone. 'And keep any of those pictures. I only took them for fun.'

'That's kind of you,' said Kate, sorting through the snaps and choosing those which she liked best. She paused. 'Have you shown them to Eliot?'

'Not yet,' said Steve, dialling.

Kate would have liked to say: don't. She knew that the pictures of herself were horribly revealing. She was looking at Eliot with the eyes of a woman in love and he could scarcely miss it in these pictures.

Hurriedly she took the ones which seemed to her most damning. At least Eliot wouldn't have the satisfaction of seeing her mooning over him in those.

Steve put her into the taxi, waved a casual hand. 'Glad you liked the pictures. 'Bye.'

The rain had stopped. The black streets, though, were empty. People were staying indoors on a night like this, and Kate couldn't blame them. She leaned back in the corner of the cab and stared at the passing lighted shop windows.

Not human, she thought again, raging. How dared

he? She looked down at the sheaf of pictures she was carrying. Oh, I'm human, she thought. I wish I wasn't.

It was eleven when she paid off the driver and walked up the silent path to the house. She got out her key and then gave a stifled little cry as something moved in the shadows beside her.

'Where the hell have you been?' Eliot asked raggedly.

She was still startled by his sudden appearance and furious because her heart was thudding. 'What's that got to do with you?' She inserted her key and opened the door, blocked him as he tried to walk inside. 'Go away!'

'Not on your life,' he muttered, pushing her inside.

She was almost speechless with fury. 'What are you doing here?' she asked, the words indistinct with temper.

'I saw the galleys and then came straight here,' Eliot bit out. 'Which brings us back to my first question: where have you been?'

She walked into the sitting-room and switched on the light. 'I had supper with Steve.'

'Steve who?' The question was terse and Eliot was staring at her fixedly.

'Martin,' she added. 'Not that it's any business of yours.'

'Steve Martin? You've been with Steve Martin?'

Kate turned on him, her teeth tight. 'Do you have to repeat everything like a parrot?'

'Don't needle me, Kate,' he said hoarsely. 'Why were you with him?'

'We had supper—I told you.'

'Supper?' Eliot was staring at her, his eyes narrow and hard.

'Yes, supper. Food. A toasted bacon sandwich, to be precise.' She looked at her watch. 'Now, if you don't mind, I'm tired.'

'Why?'

'What do you mean, why? I'm tired because it's gone eleven and I want some sleep.'

'Why did you have supper with Steve Martin?' Eliot's voice had taken on the nagging insistence of a dentist's drill.

Giving him a challenging stare, Kate asked: 'What makes it your business?'

'This,' he said savagely, catching her head in his hands.

The grinding compulsion of the kiss caught her off guard. She moaned, shaken by the force and savagery of his mouth, then closed her eyes and angrily met his rage with her own, her mouth moving fiercely against his. Eliot groaned and his arms went round her, his body clamped against hers, the kiss deepening, going from anger to sudden burning passion. Kate wound her arms round his neck and just gave up, letting the sweet, pulsating feeling take her over.

When Eliot finally stopped kissing her, he looked down at her with half-closed brilliant eyes. 'Well,' he said huskily, 'that's progress.'

Kate was too shaken to answer, leaning on him weakly, her body trembling with the emotions he had wakened. The aggression between them had burnt out within the first moment and she felt too shattered to move. The discovery she had made as she angrily kissed him back was too novel and amazing for her to be able to work out precisely what had happened to her. She only knew that the fear which had been a dominant part of her for so long had gone. It had evaporated as she let her anger flare up to meet Eliot's. By the time his violence passed into hungry passion she had been totally given over to feeling, all fear behind her.

Eliot stroked her cheek gently. 'Stopped running, darling?' he asked in an unsteady voice.

She put her face against his neck, shuddering. Desire was leaping uncontrollably inside her. She moved her lips over his skin, moaning. Eliot gave a stifled gasp and his arms tightened.

'Now tell me why you were out with Steve Martin tonight,' he said with a faint smile in his voice.

'He wanted to show me some photographs,' Kate whispered into his neck.

'And you fell for that one?' Eliot sounded furious again.

She half laughed and lifted her flushed face. 'He did!'

'Oh, of course.' Eliot's eyes flashed. 'I know him, remember. His interest in you wouldn't be photographic and you know it. You're always so quick to pick up that sort of line, so you knew too, and you went deliberately.' He caught her chin in one hand, staring at her. 'You were tormenting me again, were you?'

'What do you mean, again?' She was smiling, her blue eyes wide and bright.

'You know what I mean. You say I'm violent, Kate, but my God, I've had provocation from you. Love is a sort of rage when it's frustrated, Kate. Try putting a lid on it and it blows sky high. I'm not a violent man by nature.'

'Of course not,' she mocked, still smiling.

He smiled back drily. 'But I'll forgive you this time because you were beginning to use those rusty weapons of yours, weren't you?'

Kate was bewildered by that, her eyes opening wide and betraying it. Eliot read her puzzled face and lifted his brows. 'No? I thought you were.'

'What are you talking about?'

Amusement crept into his face. 'When you turned on me like a tigress because I'd been with Marise Filon all day it seemed so promising that I came hurrying round here to see you as soon as I got out of the office, and when you weren't here I had all sorts of mad ideas in my head.'

Her colour crept up. 'What *were* you doing all day?' she asked with a bite.

'Ah,' he said softly. 'So you admit it.'

'I admit nothing.'

'Then why have your eyes gone green?'

Kate laughed, raking her fingers deliberately through his smooth hair, and he grinned down at her. 'That's better. Admit it and I'll tell you what I've been doing.'

'Want to boast, do you?' She knew now very well that all her angry jealousy had been misplaced. Eliot's bright, satisfied eyes told her that.

'Alas,' he said mournfully, 'I had to share the lady's favours with three other men.'

'I'm sure she was equal to it!' Kate could not suppress the sting in her voice and he registered it with a broader smile.

'Puss!' He murmured it silkily, eyes glinting. 'I hope Dee isn't getting the same going-over from Judy.'

'Dee was there?'

'He insisted on it.' Eliot grinned at her. 'In fact, we had trouble keeping the numbers down. Most of the male staff volunteered. I've never known people so keen to work.'

'What did you all do?' she asked.

'Took her to lunch and then showed her London. She's an inveterate tourist. I saw sights of London I didn't know existed.'

'I bet,' Kate muttered.

He laughed and then his face changed. 'If you didn't go with Steve to drive me crazy, why did you?'

'I didn't so much go as get kidnapped,' Kate admitted, smiling. 'It was raining, so we shared a taxi and I wasn't listening to him. He talked about this and that and suddenly I was at his apartment. Without being rude I could hardly just walk off and. . .' She broke off and their eyes met. Eliot gave her a dry, comprehending smile.

'And you felt like living dangerously because you were furious with me?'

Kate eyed him, her head on one side. 'You're too quick, Mr Holman, and I don't trust you.'

'You'll learn,' he said in a light tone which did not disguise the serious emphasis behind it.

There was a pause while they looked at each other, then he asked with a faint bite, 'And what did happen? If he laid a hand on you I'll smash all his cameras.'

She laughed, shaking her head. 'Steve was a perfect gentleman.'

'It must be the first time in living memory, then,' Eliot muttered. He gave her a dry look. 'But then, as I know to my cost, you're a lady one handles with great caution.'

'I've never noticed you using much caution,' she retorted.

He grinned. 'No, and I bear the scars.'

'What a brave little soldier,' she mocked, smiling.

'But you have to admit I kept on coming,' Eliot said smoothly. 'The bullets may have whined round my ears, but they didn't stop me.'

'Great gallantry under fire,' she agreed, the blue eyes teasing him.

Eliot ruffled her black hair, smiling. 'Love me?'

The casual question made her heart stop. She heard the serious note behind it and looked at him, eyes restless. Eliot smiled at her, his face filling with passion again.

'I fell for you like a ton of bricks when I saw you standing with your shoe trapped that day,' he said quietly. 'You were so tiny and feminine, and then you suddenly swore with a fury that made me stop in my tracks. I'd been looking at you and vaguely admiring you, but the pure anger in your voice made me laugh. You do make me laugh, Kate. You've slapped me down time and time again, but you're funny with it and you keep me on my toes.'

'Thanks,' she said drily.

He laughed. 'Do you know why I never married before?'

'No one would have you,' Kate told him.

He laughed again. 'Apart from that. I never met a woman I could consider living with—I was scared of getting bored with them after a while. Living with someone is always a risk.' He stroked her cheek with a finger, smiling tenderly at her. 'One thing I am certain of—I'd never get bored with you around.'

'Well, thank you,' she said with a glinting look. 'That's a great compliment. You wouldn't be so much marrying a woman as a comedy act, I gather.'

He roared with laughter and whispered, 'Did I ask you to marry me?'

Her face filled with colour and she bit her lip. Eliot watched her, grinning.

She lifted her dark head, bristling. 'Oh, it's that sort of proposition, is it?'

'Come live with me and be my love,' he joked, his eyes amused and tender. 'I lied to you, Kate.'

She stiffened. 'Lied?'

'I said : no commitment. And I lied. I want a commitment, all right. If I could, I'd tie you down with a legal contract with sub-clauses about not looking at anyone else or moving a step from my side. But I realise you're still wary. Marriage may be out of the question for the moment, but I want you to keep it in mind. I won't rush you, I promise. I'll give you every chance to find out what sort of man you'd be getting.' His eyes mocked and invited, his hands sliding down her back. 'You can start research whenever you like.'

Her heart was moving so fast she was breathless. Desire lit a fast-burning fuse in her veins and her ears drummed. The warmth and tenderness in his face filled her eyes and she looked at him with answering passion. 'Give me time, Eliot. I want to believe you, but ...'

'That's half the battle,' he said huskily. 'Lay down your arms, Kate. I don't ask for surrender. Can't you see me waving a white flag?'

The fuse reached gunpowder and Eliot saw the flare of it light her eyes. With a muffled groan he reached for her and Kate silently gave him the surrender he had claimed he did not want. His arms wrapped urgently round her, Eliot accepted it.

Harlequin

Tender, captivating stories that sweep to faraway places and delight with the magic of love.

Exciting romance novels for the woman of today—a rare blend of passion and dramatic realism.

Sensual and romantic stories about choices, dilemmas, resolutions, and above all, the fulfillment of love.

GEN-A-2

Harlequin is romance...

INDULGE IN THE PLEASURE OF SUPERB ROMANCE READING BY CHOOSING THE MOST POPULAR LOVE STORIES IN THE WORLD

Longer, more absorbing love stories for the connoisseur of romantic fiction.

Contemporary romances—uniquely North American in flavor and appeal.

An innovative series blending contemporary romance with fast-paced adventure.

and you can never have too much romance.

What readers say about Harlequin romance fiction...

"Harlequin books are so refreshing that they take you into a different world with each one you read."

D.L.,*Jacksboro, Texas

"I hope Harlequin goes on forever."

M.Z., Hollywood, California

"Harlequin books are great; once you start reading them, you always want to read more."

T.E., Ogden, Utah

"Harlequin books bring love, happiness and romance into my very routine life."

N.J., Springfield, Missouri

*Names available on request